Nuclear Mavericks

*A Biographical Compilation of the Men
and Women Who Shaped
the Nuclear Workforce*

COMPILED BY THE
REGIONAL CENTER FOR NUCLEAR EDUCATION
AND TRAINING

This material is based upon work supported by the National Science Foundation under Grant No 1104238. Any opinions, findings, conclusions or recommendations expressed in this material are those of the author(s) and do not necessarily reflect the views of the National Science Foundation.

Published by Indian River State College

ISBN: 978-0-692-54012-1

Cover designed by Christopher Wright
Interior designed by Illumination Graphics

TABLE OF CONTENTS

FOREWORD

◆

FIRST, THANK YOU FOR PICKING UP THIS BOOK. I HOPE YOU ENJOY THE stories and leave a little wiser. I know you will be proud of the mavericks who helped form America's nuclear industry.

This book is the result of four years of discussion with nuclear pioneers. These subject matter experts, or SMEs, have built and lived the nuclear culture. Their knowledge, know-how, and skills will be invaluable to the next generation of nuclear industry workers gearing up to take their places.

A little history is relevant here. In 2011, the National Science Foundation (NSF) awarded funding to the Regional Center for Nuclear Education and Training (RCNET) for the development of a standardized pipeline of nuclear technicians across the nation through a program called the Advanced Technological Education, or ATE, Division.

The ATE Division was created in October 1992, when Congress passed the Scientific and Advanced Technology Act, known by its acronym, SATA. President George H. W. Bush signed the legislation on October 23, making it Public Law 102-476. Its sponsors included North Carolina Congressman David Price and Maryland Senator Barbara A. Mikulski. Price, a Duke University political science professor before his election to Congress, wanted the NSF to support workforce issues in a way that complemented the Department of Education's tech-prep activities and the Department of Labor's short-term training. Mikulski, a social worker before she began her political career on Baltimore's City Council, wanted government investments in high-tech fields to include economic development for diverse populations.

The American Association of Community Colleges (AACC), then known as the American Association of Community and Junior Colleges, had lobbied Congress for years to get the NSF to pay more attention to community colleges. Then, as now, community colleges educate nearly half of the nation's undergraduates. The AACC engaged professional societies in its effort to obtain federal help to improve math and science programs at two-year colleges. Meetings of experts were convened and reports issued. Perhaps the most important of the various meetings on the subject was the Workshop on Science, Engineering, and Mathematics Education, which convened on May 13–14, 1991 sponsored by the NSF. The report from this workshop, *Matching Actions and Challenges*, influenced several people who later shaped the ATE program.

SATA was one of the first mandates Congress ever gave the NSF; typically, the NSF tells Congress what it wants to do. Approximately twenty years later, the NSF ATE program is as strong as ever, operating with a budget of over $60 million and supporting programs and centers at over thirty-five community colleges and universities.

In 2011, the NSF recognized that, as a result of retirement, the size of the nuclear workforce was shrinking—and that the next generation of nuclear workers needed to be trained. The RCNET was created to help meet this need; its mission is to aid in the development and sustainability of a highly technical and skilled workforce pipeline for the nuclear fields of energy, environmental management, life and plant sciences, and manufacturing.

Along the way, we, at RCNET, have done a great job working with over 160 industry, agency, college, and university partners, training over six hundred educators, and helping over two thousand graduate students complete nuclear programs. Our resources have been used by thousands of future nuclear workers and our materials have been employed at hundreds of institutions. We have collaborated regularly with industry and agency leaders over the past four years and gained a deeper understanding of their needs along the way. It is a result of these long-term collaborations that this book emerged.

The nuclear industry was pleased with the quality of the technicians we were providing. RCNET graduates had fundamental knowledge, hands-on skills, and most importantly, they were acclimated to the nuclear culture—but a large limitation was identified – they lacked a sense of pride and ownership in their work.

The mavericks who developed the various nuclear tracks poured their blood, sweat, and tears into the field, literally building it from the ground up. As in many family businesses, however, the generation that inherited their work didn't exhibit the same level of ownership.

How could the next generation be taught pride and ownership? Can such attitudes even be taught?

The idea behind this collection had its beginnings in an epiphany that came over us while sharing glasses of wine with a couple of nuclear pioneers. Perhaps, if we could get readers to see through the eyes of an eclectic mix of nuclear mavericks, they would connect with their tales and emerge with a little more knowledge about and pride in the feats accomplished by the nuclear forefathers. Although these mavericks had no roadmaps or clearly defined pathways at their disposal, they all exhibit extreme pride in their industry and field.

From their stories, you will experience how they worked from the ground up to build their fields into great legacies for the next generation. Some were intentional journeys, and others developed happenstance; however, each of them was the result of hard work, dedication, and excellence. It is this sense of pride and ownership that our mavericks wish to share, and impart, to you. I hope you enjoy reading this volume as much as we have enjoyed putting it together. In closing, we'd like to thank the mavericks for letting us showcase them and NSF for funding this work.

—Kevin Cooper, PhD, Principal Investigator, RCNET

INTRODUCTION

◆

FOR THE FIRST TIME, LARGE GENERAL AUDIENCES ARE WITNESSING actual demonstrations of controlled nuclear fusion, a scientific development of major significance in man's quest of new energy sources. Each demonstration—there is one every six minutes—is a full scientific experiment in which fusion reactions are achieved by the same techniques that have been used for studying these processes at the General Electric Research Laboratory.

Here is the climax of the Progressland visit. Everyone looks intently at the large quartz tube atop the fusion equipment at the bottom of the centerwell. The countdown ends. There is a sudden brilliant burst of light . . . and a crash of discharging high voltage that echoes and re-echoes through the centerwell. You have just seen one of the first public demonstrations of fusion—the energy source that may someday supply all the electricity we'll ever need. Much new knowledge, many new skills, are needed before sustained fusion power can be realized on a large scale. But General Electric has made a beginning.

—General Electric's Progressland Pavilion
at the 1964 New York World's Fair

For over a century—more than fifty years before General Electric's public demonstration in Flushing Meadows, New York, and more than fifty years since—nuclear science has been the stuff of legend. It has held the promise of producing vast amounts of cheap and reliable electrical power for peacetime use. Today, in many parts of the world, nuclear science is delivering on that promise, and more. Nuclear technology has been applied to the diagnosis of diseases and injuries, the sterilization of medical equipment, and the treatment of many medical conditions. In an increasing number of cases, nuclear technology is used to manufacture things we use every day. For example, radiation has replaced sulfur in the process of vulcanizing tires, and food irradiation represents an alternative to current methods of food preservation. Other applications abound.

Quietly, nuclear technology has become an important part of the world economy, and it has done so in ways that are surprising to many people. In the United States, nuclear power plants produce 20 percent of all electric power from all sources. In many countries, this percentage is much higher.

France generates 75 percent of its electricity from nuclear energy; Switzerland produces nearly 38 percent of its power from nuclear plants. In South Korea, this figure is just over 30 percent. Worldwide, there are over 430 nuclear plants in operation today, with another 60 or more under construction. Still, because of the geographic size of the United States and its vast economy, American nuclear power plants are responsible for over 30 percent of the world's total nuclear power, the largest of any country in the world. But what is even more remarkable is the large number of people employed in America's nuclear industries and the diverse fields in which they work.

While four hundred thousand individuals are employed in nuclear power generation, four *million* are employed in medical and industrial applications of nuclear technology, primarily in the use of radiation. Beyond these "routine," though impressive, applications of nuclear technology, there are examples of its power and potential that rival science fiction.

Nuclear submarines run silently below our oceans, as do huge surface ships equipped with onboard reactors. A research station in Antarctica was powered for years by its own nuclear generator. The space program constantly develops new applications of nuclear energy for both manned and unmanned missions. And nuclear medicine, which uses nuclear technology in many applications today, promises more amazing discoveries. Few industries can compete with the nuclear industry's wide variety of career and growth opportunities.

And yet, despite these impressive statistics, many Americans still see nuclear power in a negative light. One reason is the way nuclear power was "born" in the twentieth century—as a weapon of mass destruction, to use today's terminology. The Manhattan Project's impressive advances in nuclear science for example, resulted in the explosion of two bombs over Japan.

In the following decades, the Cold War was based on the United States and Russia's shared capacity to annihilate each other, if not the entire world, with nuclear weapons. The events of September 11, 2001, reminded us how vulnerable our country is to terrorist attacks, and they highlighted the possibility that a future event might involve a nuclear weapon. Public fear of nuclear science has been stoked by fictional books and films, speculative news coverage, and unfortunately, a handful of real-life disasters. It's disappointing, but not surprising, that more Americans are familiar with Three Mile Island, Chernobyl, and Fukushima than they are with the success stories of the nuclear power industry.

But here's the bottom line: nuclear energy is safer than ever, and it is getting safer every day. There is evidence that nuclear power plants are less risky than plants relying on oil, coal, and natural gas; pollution from nuclear plants is nearly nonexistent, and the risks associated with obtaining fuel are far lower than those of traditional fossil fuel power plants. Nuclear plants have also proven remarkably reliable.

In the cases of Hurricane Andrew and Hurricane Sandy, nuclear power plants were still in operation after these storms—and were the only source of electricity for many communities. Perhaps most importantly, as the people telling their stories here will point out, professionals in the nuclear industry have demonstrated a solid commitment to "safety first" and have allocated enormous resources to the education and training of people employed in this exciting field. Because the consequences associated with the risk of accidents are so serious, serious emphasis has been placed on the application of computer technology, the development of redundancies to ensure continuous safe operation in the event of malfunctions, and—most importantly—the willingness of everyone in the industry to learn from one another's mistakes. As a result, the nuclear industry is on its way to boasting a great safety record. Eventually, leaders in the industry believe, this good news will outweigh the fears of nuclear power that have been ingrained in the American public for decades, whether such fears are rooted in actual accidents, urban myths, or outright fiction. Employees in the nuclear field know it is a safe industry in which to work. They know it provides real contributions to today's society. And, most importantly, they know it holds real promise for tomorrow.

Therein lies the story of this book. The science behind today's nuclear-energy generation, and the myriad ways in which nuclear technology is being applied in other industries, is really a story about *people*. There would be no science without scientists, and there would be no nuclear industry without the exceptional people who have made it their profession.

As the industry grows, it will offer new and exciting career opportunities for young people. Like any relatively new field of human endeavor, the application of nuclear technology is a place where individuals can make their own mark; it has a rich tradition of pioneers who have made, and who are continuing to make, contributions that could not have been foreseen even a few years before they became reality. This was true for people like Albert Einstein, Ernest Rutherford, and Marie Curie. It is also true for pioneers like J. Robert Oppenheimer, Admiral Hyman Rickover, and Hans Bethe. And, as we will see, it is true for the nine people whose personal stories are included in this book.

They've shared their life lessons in the hope that they will inspire future pioneers in the fascinating field of nuclear science. And they've done so from a broad range of perspectives. As you'll see, the "heroes" of this book aren't just physicists. They're metallurgists, managers, machinists, and midshipmen. They're men and women just like anyone else considering a career in any field. And they can't offer enough words of encouragement to those interested in following in their footsteps. Read on. Enjoy what they've shared, and learn from their experiences. Perhaps one day, your story will be included in the history of the nuclear industry.

A BRIEF HISTORY OF THE NUCLEAR INDUSTRY

◆

THE SCIENCE WE NOW CALL "NUCLEAR PHYSICS" BEGAN AT THE END of the nineteenth century with a series of discoveries made by physicists as they experimented with cathode rays. Actually, when cathode rays — streams of electrons sent through glass vacuum tubes — are included in the history of nuclear science, this timeline could be stretched back to the 1860s and 1870s and the work of German scientists Johann Hittorf and Eugen Goldstein (who coined the term *cathode ray* in 1876). In 1895, Wilhelm Roentgen, also a German, discovered an unknown ray by accident, which he called the *X-ray*. Six years later, he received the Nobel Prize for his pioneering work.

Physicists continued to rack up Nobel prizes, though some of the discoveries began purely by accident. In 1896, in France, Antoine Henri Becquerel found that uranium could darken a photographic plate, which led to the discovery of radioactivity. The same year, Pierre and Marie Curie discovered natural radioactivity, for which they shared the 1903 Nobel Prize. In 1897, the British scientist J. J. Thompson discovered the electron while doing his work on cathode rays; he would receive the 1906 Nobel Prize for his discovery.

In 1899, Ernest Rutherford, considered the father of nuclear physics, was able to define radioactivity as the by-product of one element transforming into another, and he developed the concept of half-life to quantify the process. In 1902, he co-published a theory of nuclear decay (and later won the 1908 Nobel Prize). The nineteenth-century dawn of nuclear physics concluded with the coining of the term *isotope* in 1900 by Frederick Soddy, to help describe the "transmutation" of certain radioactive elements. His published works, which spanned the first half of the twentieth century, included *The Interpretation of Radium* (1909) and *Atomic Transmutation* (1953). Soddy won the 1921 Nobel Prize.

And, while some may argue it is not as central to nuclear science as is popularly believed, Albert Einstein published his special theory of relativity (e = mc²) in 1905. He introduced the concept that energy and matter are one and the same and can be converted from one to the other. In 1915, Einstein published the general theory of relativity, which described how the speed of light could be affected by forces such as gravity and motion.

Einstein's theories were highly controversial at the time; many of his peers went to great lengths to disprove his work. Einstein's reservations about quantum theory—he argued the theories advanced by Erwin Schrodinger needed to be "completed"—also alienated him from other physicists. Many of Einstein's peers wanted simply to run with Schrodinger's theory and were consequently dismissive of Einstein's objection to it as being "spooky." (Einstein later contributed to the development of quantum mechanics by Schrodinger and Max Born.)

After being nominated for over a decade, Einstein received the Nobel Prize in 1921, two years after British astrophysicist Arthur Eddington verified Einstein's theory by observing the deflection of sunlight during a total eclipse. Einstein (like Max Born and James Franck) came to the United States to continue his work.

The science of nuclear physics continued with Niels Bohr's 1913 publication of the first theory of atomic structure and its incorporation of quantum theory, along with Rutherford and the world's first manmade nuclear reaction in 1917. When Bohr won the 1922 Nobel Prize in Physics, he acknowledged the work of Einstein in his acceptance speech.

In 1929, Ernest O. Lawrence invented the cyclotron; the same year, John Cockcroft and E. T. S. Walton created the first "linear accelerator." All three won Nobel Prizes for their work in accelerating protons and the resulting improvements in physicists' ability to study nuclear reactions.

James Chadwick discovered the neutron in 1932, which led to his Nobel Prize in 1935. Also in 1935, Italian physicist Enrico Fermi announced he had produced "the first transuranic element" by irradiating uranium with neutrons; in fact, scientists later recognized his achievement as the first nuclear fission; Fermi won the 1938 Nobel Prize for this inadvertent but historic discovery. Hans Bethe, studying fusion, theorized in 1938 that this type of nuclear reaction actually powered the sun (he would go on to win the 1967 Nobel Prize for this discovery).

In 1939, scientists in many countries studied nuclear fission; in October of that year, Albert Einstein wrote a letter to President Franklin Roosevelt suggesting the possibility of a uranium bomb. Roosevelt authorized the Manhattan Project two years later.

As World War II raged, scientists in England, Germany, and the United States were all pursuing the possibility of building the world's first nuclear weapon. In 1941, the American Glenn Seaborg discovered plutonium, and a committee of British physicists reported a nuclear weapon could be built with twenty-two pounds of uranium-235. A year later, Fermi, now at the University of Chicago, created the first controlled nuclear fission reactor.

In September 1942, under the direction of Brigadier General Leslie Groves and Scientific Director J. Robert Oppenheimer, the Manhattan Project began operations; the following March, Oppenheimer moved the project to a secret facility in Los Alamos, New Mexico. As the world's scientists continued their rush to invent nuclear weapons, physicist Niels Bohr left Copenhagen in 1943 for the United States and joined the Manhattan Project in December.

Bohr believed the possibility of worldwide destruction from a nuclear war could spark international cooperation on the control of nuclear weapons, and he proposed informing the Soviets as the first step toward fostering cooperation and world peace once the war ended. He took his proposal first to Churchill, who rejected it outright, and then to Roosevelt, who seemed more amenable to the idea. Eventually, Roosevelt came around to Churchill's point of view, and Bohr was investigated to ensure he wasn't passing secrets to the Soviets on his own. With the liberation of Denmark from the Nazis, Bohr returned to Copenhagen in June 1945, continuing his work on the control of nuclear weapons for the rest of his life.

The success of the Manhattan Project, the consequent bombing of Hiroshima and Nagasaki, and the end of World War II remain vivid memories of 1945. To people the world over, these events mark the beginning of the Nuclear Age. For decades, science-fiction movies from Japan featured dinosaurs and other prehistoric beasts destroying cities after being awakened from hibernation deep within the earth by nuclear radiation. Suburban homeowners in the United States built fallout shelters in their basements and beneath their backyards, and schoolchildren participated in "duck and cover" drills during class.

These popular phenomena clouded the true nature of nuclear science and contributed to an exaggerated fear of the consequences of peaceful applications of nuclear technology—electric power generation, ship propulsion, space exploration, medical science, and manufacturing. Science, of course, continued to advance despite these distractions, and contributions resulting from the work of nuclear professionals the world over continued to accumulate.

These individuals—the "nuclear mavericks" whose stories make up this book—are today's versions of the Nobel Prize winners whose contributions marked the first fifty years of progress in an industry brimming with potential for even more astonishing peaceful applications. Some of these mavericks began their careers with the original nuclear pioneers as their teachers and mentors and all of them have lessons to share about their careers and discoveries. They offer advice for the people who will follow them, much as they followed the Einsteins, Bohrs, and Rutherfords of decades past.

Their stories, at first glance, may not seem as momentous as the stories of these Nobel Prize winners, but remember Einstein was criticized by his peers and remained in his day job in the German Patent Office for several years after the publication of his theories of relativity. Bohr's advice was rejected by Churchill and Roosevelt. As a means of escaping fascist Italy, Enrico Fermi had to take his family—and his whole life—with him to Stockholm to accept his Nobel Prize in 1938. These pioneers lived their lives in the present, as all of us do: it is only through the lens of history that much of their greatness is appreciated. Similarly, the nine people whose stories are detailed here may view their achievements merely as part of a job they were paid to do; while future generations may praise their work as something that made the world a better place.

These mavericks have chosen their careers in the nuclear industry or, in some cases, have been chosen for that career by chance or through the wise decisions of others. They also live their lives in the present, meeting new challenges as they arise, moving from one location to another to pursue their personal and professional dreams, and taking stock of their long careers to pass on their knowledge and experience. Most simply wanted to do their jobs well, be remembered and respected by their peers, and be loved by their families.

But these are wonderful life goals as well. Their stories are compelling tales of scientific discovery, hard work, and team effort, and remarkable examples of the confluence of individual careers with world events. Today's Nuclear Age is, in many ways, no different from the world in which the first nuclear physicists made their marks.

The characters in this book are real individuals; their stories are true. Their accomplishments are often quietly remarkable, and the lessons they have to teach us are profound. As a group, they may not have the same number of Nobel Prizes the first generation of atomic physicists won a century ago. But they are the nuclear mavericks of today, carrying on a unique and distinguished tradition. There is no telling which of the people in this book will become famous for their work; perhaps none will. But they have shared their stories in order for the next generation of nuclear pioneers to understand the passion, the dedication, and most importantly, the sense of ownership required to be one of the nuclear mavericks of tomorrow.

CHAPTER 1

◆

VIRGIL COX

Dean, Engineering and Industrial Technologies Gaston College

Nuclear power plants are great places to work. That sounds ridiculous, but they are. You are absolutely, 100 percent safe at a nuclear plant.

VIRGIL COX STARTED HIS CAREER IN THE NAVY IN 1956, working mostly in electronics and communication. About a year later, the Soviets launched Sputnik, "and the Navy got all disturbed about the fact that they didn't have a sufficient number of people with technical educations," he remembers. In response, the Navy started a program to train enlistees in technical areas, and Cox signed on. As part of the program, he was sent to MIT for four years, where he studied nuclear physics. After his time at MIT, Cox worked for none other than Admiral Hyman Rickover, the "Father of the Nuclear Navy."

"SURVIVING" ADMIRAL RICKOVER

Cox recalls, "I survived one of Rickover's interview sessions, and they were notorious." Many people from the nuclear industry at this time can share hair-raising stories about those interviews. Rickover was famous for having abrupt interactions with people considering going into nuclear power.

When the interviewee arrived, he would be briefed and then sent to a little cubicle where, sometime later, a commander or a captain would come get him. Cox says, "They would take you into his office, which wasn't really big. Rather than having a normal desk, Rickover had a table raised about six inches off the floor. You would sit down in a chair that had a couple of inches cut off of the front two legs, so it rocked you forward and brought your knees up to your chest as you faced the Admiral. The commander or captain who brought you there stayed in the room, and, if you didn't answer the questions as quickly as Rickover thought you should, or he was irritated about how you were functioning, it was the commander's job to get you out of the office. You would then be taken back to a cubicle, and you might sit there for two minutes or two hours. If Rickover decided he wanted to continue questioning you, you would go back in; otherwise, you would go back to where you came from. It was pretty notorious."

It wasn't uncommon for people to spend hours later contemplating, "What did I do wrong in there?" But Cox's experience wasn't the norm. "My interview with him was just totally a nonevent. He asked me a few simple questions like why was I at MIT, and why did I study physics. That was it," Cox says. "I survived."

AN ONGOING TRADITION OF "SAFETY FIRST"

Cox understands why Rickover was so hard on those trying to enter his field. As the face of the industry, the Admiral obviously wanted the best of the best. Further, according to Cox, Rickover did everything he could to avoid casting Navy nuclear power in a negative public light. And he noted there were a couple of reasons why Rickover could get away with being difficult and intimidating. "His administrative structure was a mile wide, but only one inch deep," Cox explains, "No one in nuclear power, even those without an officer rank, was probably more than one or two people away from being able to communicate with him directly." There was always immediate access to him to ensure that things were being done in the right way. Cox believes Rickover's goal was to make sure that decisions were being vetted constantly, so no one ever put the Navy or nuclear power in any kind of jeopardy. It was very much "safety first" and everything else came second.

Although Cox had never connected the dots before, he thinks Rickover's philosophy is reflected in his own career and even his personal life. "I don't run a risky life. As I think about my decisions, what I would do in any situation, all of them are pretty much guaranteed to be relatively risk-free," he says, laughing, "even though, with human behavior, everything's always risky."

Looking back, though, Cox sees that Rickover was willing to make risky decisions on his own, but only after considerable thought about how things might play out. Cox recalls one exception – a situation where the nuclear Navy was conducting a power run on an S1G, the shore-based equivalent of the reactor system used in the USS Nautilus (the world's first operational nuclear-powered submarine). Most likely, planning ahead to avoid the political ramifications of what he was doing, Rickover made a decision to change standard procedure. Cox says, "Part of the whole safety system is you do not change procedures without having the change vetted elsewhere. Change a procedure? No, no, no, no!"

Rickover knew the possible political consequences for taking such a risk. He was willing to take some risk himself, though he would never allow that of anyone else. Whenever possible, if there was something in a test or a procedure that didn't look right, the solution was to go into safe mode and find out why.

And Rickover's approach worked. The Navy has avoided catastrophic events such as the 1979 Three Mile Island crisis. Cox explains, "In the nuclear power business, Three Mile Island is a memorable nuclear accident, which became a watershed for civilian nuclear power. Because of it, we ended up with major political changes."

Most people seem to focus strictly on what the nuclear industry learned about what *not* to do in that type of situation. But Cox sees it somewhat differently, "What happened there was a personnel failure, a training failure." He believes the disaster's primary lesson for the public nuclear power business was one they should have learned without an accident. Quite simply, they could not run a nuclear power plant with the philosophy of control being used by coal power steam plants at that time, which wasn't a "safety first" approach.

He offers an example. When he was a crewmember on the Nautilus [USS Nautilus, SSN571] in 1964, the nuclear submarine was in overhaul in Portsmouth, New Hampshire, being fitted with a new core. To get the vessel back out of the shipyard, myriad tests were required. The crew had to light off the reactor, spin the prop, and carry out other essential operations.

When the testing procedures were under way, "We went critical," Cox says. The sub was within a few hundred yards of civilian property, but nobody in the area was worried. "Twenty-five miles south of there, at Seabrook, people were lying in the road to keep the civilian Seabrook nuclear power plant from being built. But here we were, just north, at a shipyard, with a nuclear power system possibly malfunctioning. But because of the way the Navy managed its nuclear program, with its 'safety first' approach, we didn't have the civilian protests," Cox says. The entire shipyard, which included a thousand people who lived in Kittery, knew the sub was going critical, but few grew concerned because they were confident the Navy knew how to safely handle the potential crisis.

Safety first has a long history in the Navy—a history the industrial world doesn't necessarily have. During World War I, if a submarine's surfacings weren't equal to its dives, it was considered a "bad day," in Cox's parlance, language indicating the actual loss of the submarine – an event when something terrible happened inside a submarine and it never returned.

The Navy wanted to make certain the risks of "bad days" based on "terrible" events were minimized. Submariners set up procedures for safety. Although post – World War II submarines were diesel subs, they were the same vessels into which nuclear cores were initially installed. The submarine crews were accustomed to procedures designed to make certain they operated as safely as possible.

Cox points out that one of the lessons learned from Three Mile Island was the civilian nuclear industry should study and adapt Naval training for nuclear facilities; setting up systems with "safety first" as the primary goal. It took time for the civilian nuclear industry to adapt, but Cox is confident they have.

Before Three Mile Island, each nuclear company was functioning as an independent group, responsible for vetting its own processes and safety. Three Mile Island clearly illuminated the fact that the industry wasn't vetting things properly. After that incident, the civilian industry recognized safety had to be paramount, and procedures were set up that included cross-communication assessment, incident report-

ing, and INPO (Institute of Nuclear Power Operations) training and oversight.

Today, nuclear power is one of the few industries in the
United States where all companies involved know nearly
everything with regard to what the other companies are
doing. If something goes wrong and a power plant incident
occurs, a system is now in place to ensure every other plant
knows the details. Information is captured and shared; the
problem is corrected. That information is also disseminated
to other companies and plants, and the possibility of a similar
occurrence is minimized.

"However," Cox points out, "The safety first approach is
not international. At least, I don't think it's as rigid or as powerful or as universally accepted as it is in the United States."
Unfortunately, the Fukushima incident in 2011 is an extremely good example.

Cox wonders why Fukushima was built on the tsunami side
of Japan. If the planners had considered all the safety risks this
location presented, they would have placed it on the other side
of Japan, where they don't have tsunamis like the one that wiped
out Fukushima.

When asked why he believes Fukushima was chosen for the
nuclear plant, Cox replies, "It was an economic decision. There
was an existing nuclear power plant located significantly higher
off the surface of the ocean than Fukushima. But, economically,
Fukushima was a better location." The other power plant is located between the epicenter of the earthquake and Fukushima,
and that power plant worked perfectly. Many sound decisions
led to this other plant being the safer one to operate.

In Cox's opinion, the United States' "safety first" approach
will eventually be emulated by the rest of the world, where nuclear power has been a major source of energy for quite a while.

Cox feels that looking forward, nuclear power can't be ignored. He points out, "If it's run the way it's run in the United States, it is a safe, appropriate way for getting base power for a country or a region."

A LIFETIME OF TRAINING

When Cox was stationed on the Nautilus, he had completed MIT nuclear training, submarine training, nuclear power school, and he had qualified on the D1G nuclear power plant. He explains, once a person was selected to go into the nuclear Navy, he would undergo six months of classroom training to learn the basics of nuclear power systems. Then he would be sent to a shore-based nuclear power plant that simulated a destroyer or a submarine and be trained on the type of reactor providing the onboard electricity generation and propulsion.

At the power plant, trainees for nuclear Navy operations were trained and qualified on every operating station, performing on plants similar to those on Navy vessels.

Cox says, "There was hardly a switch or a valve you did not have to know where it was and what it did; it was just an enormous amount of information that you had to have. Then you had to know all of the procedures involved in lighting off the plant, running the plant, shutting off the plant, turning on the plant, etc. There were emergency procedures, like what happens if that switch opens and you lose your main feed pumps, or if you lose a condensate pump, or a steam generator shuts down, all sorts of things. It was a very rigorous operational training program."

Before trainees were done; rigorous testing had to be completed. In order to be qualified, they performed a standing watch, completed testing on procedures as an operator, and faced an oral board. At the oral board, trainees were grilled for an hour or more on how to respond in any situation. "How do you do it? Which way does it turn? Really detailed stuff," Cox remembers. "Those who didn't pass were sent back to the regular Navy, and, to my knowledge, there was no retread [retesting]. So you worked your butt off."

Cox recalls, "It isn't that those people were in any way flawed; they were intelligent. They just got to the point where they weren't appropriate for nuclear work. They were fine candidates for many other naval positions, and many went on to successful careers – just not in the nuclear Navy."

Cox's formal educational training included his four years at MIT, six months at Ballston Spa in the simulated trainer, six months of submarine school, and another six months of nuclear school. It was a total of five-and-a-half years of traditional training before he was assigned to a vessel.

Today's educational requirements are similar. Now, enlistees hoping to join the nuclear Navy go through basic nuclear school, receive basic operator training at a plant, and then are assigned to a ship. They are not provided the four years of formal education that Cox received, though he does point out that most officers have the additional four years of secondary education under their belts already, and many of the others have two years at a community college or the equivalent. But Cox's training didn't stop after his five-and-a-half years. When asked how long his training did last, Cox says, "Twenty years!"

Training was, and still is, a constant part of the job, because nuclear technology is continually advancing. During active deployment at sea, Navy men and women continually practice various kinds of drills.

"I guess it's a similar answer that you might get from a professional athlete if you asked, 'When did you play basketball? Was it only when you were playing another team?'" Cox says. "No, you're playing basketball all the time, always practicing and learning new things. We're professional nuclear officers, and we were constantly making sure we knew what to do when we were at sea."

NUCLEAR POWER IS A POLITICAL ISSUE

Cox is a strong proponent of safe nuclear energy as a power source. Nuclear power may be considered "greener" than other fuels. Cox comments, "Ultimately, we have to solve the spent-fuel problem, but to a large extent, I think the use of nuclear energy is much more of a political problem than an actual physical problem. And politics screws things up everywhere."

He believes the negative perception of nuclear energy can be improved by the industry setting ever-higher standards of its commitment to quality and safety.

Improvements in technology will also go a long way.

When Rickover and his group designed the first Nautilus reactor, they used technology people don't even talk about anymore, such as magnetic amplifiers, or mag amps, electromagnetic devices for amplifying electrical signals.

Cox acknowledges the technology used on the first nuclear plants was extremely stable, even though, as he says, "We knew it was 'old-timey,' in a way." Now equipment is computer-based, which means it can respond much more quickly than a human being. In addition, he points out today's electronics use redundancy to ensure that if a circuit breaks, for example, another takes over within a millionth of a second, cuts out the bad circuit, and replaces it, always maintaining full operations. "We couldn't do that back in 1960, you know," Cox explains, "The only way we knew there was a problem was because a red light went on, indicating that a circuit just died, and we were now on backup."

But public perception, and the political reaction to it, takes a long time to change. In the past twenty years, there has been little construction of power plants and reactors in the United States. The Navy is an exception. Cox points out the military was adding to their plants but the civilian industry was not in the position to take that risk. There's an enormous amount of preliminary work and expense that goes into creating a nuclear power plant.

"We seemed to be stuck in the '80s for a while," he says. "But I personally think it's getting unstuck now, it's beginning to break loose. I believe we're moving into an age in which, with the new technologies and overall increase in safety, there is definitely a future for the nuclear power plant."

With new legislation coming into effect requiring the tightening of emissions standards (beginning in 2017), nuclear energy, by necessity, is going to be playing a bigger role in America's power-generation capabilities. Cox acknowledges for a while natural gas will be plentiful and may become a primary source of energy. And, although the country is moving away from it, there is still a lot of coal available. But he points out – gas won't last forever and it does have some negative effects. Cox says, "Yes, right now, gas is cheap. But the whole fracking thing is very political. And I'm not sure enough safety measures have gone into place for the fracking process." He strongly believes the effects from nuclear power plants are safer than those which result from fracking for natural gas.

In fact, he points out that this country has years' worth of power just sitting in casks of "spent" fuel. "We just need to separate out the good stuff, take care of the stuff we don't want, and recycle the fuel that's there back into the system. We don't even have to mine for more of it." Cox believes that ultimately we will get to use the "spent" fuel we have accumulated and nuclear power will become our major source of energy.

When asked if he would be comfortable living next to a plant, Cox says emphatically, "Knowing what I know, yeah. Those places are not going to explode, that's all there is to it." That's the public misconception he sees—people are confused about the connection between nuclear energy, the nuclear industry as a whole, and atomic bombs.

Cox points out that a lot of the anti-nuclear groups have yet to understand what the industry's latest technology can do to keep people safe and they aren't willing to trust it. Again, there isn't an acknowledgement of the difference between nuclear energy and nuclear weapons. "I think that's where the fear is created," Cox says.

NUCLEAR POWER AS A CAREER FOR THE NEW GENERATION

Cox asks the following, "What question do high school guidance counselors normally ask a student who walks into their office?" The best question he heard was, "What do you want to be when you grow up?"

"That's a good one," he says. "But that isn't the common question today. What most students report to me that they are asked is, 'What school do you want to go to?'"

To Cox, the truth is there are really only two types of post-secondary education – those that are occupationally oriented and "everything else."

Students can major in a general study ("everything else") and ultimately find an occupation, but they end up having to learn how to do the work, hoping four years of college has trained them to learn fast and be successful in whatever career they eventually pursue. Occupationally oriented education is designed to help students become exactly what they have been trained to do.

It also means students in these educational programs have to focus on the occupations within a certain industry, to choose which ones will suit them and sustain their interest throughout their careers. Most students intend to earn a living through their education, but many end up at graduation wondering, "What do I do now?'"

Cox is now the Dean of Engineering and Industrial Technologies at Gaston College, part of the North Carolina Community College system and a partner of Duke Energy. As an educator, he has to understand the occupations in technological industries, as well as the prospects for employment in those occupations.

Cox and his staff strive to design programs that will help train today's students for tomorrow's jobs, so he needs to understand exactly what type of experience and training will be needed. "People come to me and say, 'I need somebody with this knowledge and this experience,' and I ask them to tell me about the experience in more detail."

The employers often want someone who can operate a new piece of equipment, but when Cox asks for a donation of the equipment in order to train his students, they say, "No. It costs a billion bucks." Rather than being stymied by that response, Cox and his team at Gaston have created the first nuclear technology apprentice-type program in the state. It is one of few programs like it in the country.

Cox notes there has been a resurgence of nuclear education across the United States, but that doesn't mean that a lot of young people are applying. "The nuclear power program here at Gaston is four years old. We get fifteen people a year expressing interest in it. Ultimately some go into maintenance and some go into operations." He readily admits his school could handle more students.

Cox sees a bright future for students choosing a career in nuclear energy, but he's concerned whether there will be enough graduates to cover the emerging jobs. For many years, there was a sufficient number of retirees from military nuclear programs to adequately staff positions in civilian nuclear power; in fact, these retirees were the primary source of staffing for the nuclear industry. But that's no longer the case. As many in the industry are realizing, these people are aging and retiring, and soon there won't be enough upcoming graduates and retirees to replace their ranks. According to Cox, the rate of current graduates is meeting the nuclear industry's needs right now. But with more plants coming online, new positions will be opening up and staff shortages may follow.

The most serious problem may not be the need for new employees or the capability of education and training programs to deliver them. It will be the inadequate number of students who choose to enter the field, which is where years of negative public opinion of nuclear power come into play.

Cox's message to potential students who may be concerned about the dangers involved with jobs in the nuclear industry is, "Nuclear power plants are great places to work. That sounds ridiculous, but they are. You are absolutely, 100 percent safe at a nuclear plant." He expands on the truth of his statement, "Say you punch the wrong code into a secure doorway—within seconds, probably less, you are visited by an armed guard. That's the level of safety everywhere in the industry. One of the ladies I work with at Duke Energy was on the midnight shift for many years and she was constantly asked if she really felt safe. Her response is, 'Yes, I feel safe. With the armed guards and the safety of the systems in place, there's nobody coming through that fence to cause me or the plant any trouble.'"

The "safety first" values of the industry assure that the people who work at nuclear power plants dutifully follow all procedures. Cox notes there are even "'change protocols' for what to do when you detect the designated procedure is not taking you where you want to go. Of course you need to follow those change protocols as carefully as you follow any other procedure at a nuclear power plant. It's a natural consequence of "safety first." The quickest way to get fired is to violate one of those procedures. I think the industry has learned its lessons well. It's important to keep those electrons going down the grid, and it's even more important to make sure everything is safe going forward."

Cox also warns newcomers to the nuclear industry of the commitment it requires, "You'd better be dedicated to the job! There are many challenges in getting a position and you have to really want to work in the industry. If you aren't fully committed, you probably ought to go elsewhere."

Before deciding to become a nuclear worker, each potential applicant needs to consider some of the consequences whichthat come with the job, and be ready to deal with them. Cox stresses, "Jobs in this industry require concentration. They require dedication."

And the training is tough. The four nuclear power courses at Gaston are considered four of the most difficult courses on campus to pass. "You really have no business coming out of one of those with a C average," he warns. "That might get you into certain places, but it won't get you into nuclear operations. Remember, jobs in this industry require constant training and constant vigilance."

If you can't excel in courses in nuclear power and aren't prepared to maintain total focus, then you probably aren't nuclear material. But if you are, Cox promises your career path will be interesting, rewarding, and memorable.

LESSONS LEARNED

■ Safety first! The nuclear culture is one of safety. You must take all the safety procedures seriously and understand their importance.

■ Procedure protocols have to be followed meticulously, as any mishaps could jeopardize the entire nuclear fleet.

■ Training is continuous. You will be challenged to learn new skills and procedures all the time.

■ Transparency and redundancy of systems are key to limiting the potential of a plant incident.

CHAPTER 2

◆

STACEY SMITH PRESNELL

Instructional Technologist/Nuclear Technology Program
Coordinator Energy Northwest

*We must educate the next generation, first in the classroom, and
then by bringing them into the power plant for on-the-job
training. It's so important that we can have that knowledge
transfer from the older generation.*

GROWING UP IN NORTHERN IDAHO, STACEY SMITH PRESNELL WAS A
fortunate little girl. She was raised by a father who loved his
thirty years as a wildfire and control burn specialist for the Forest
Service, a stepmother whose unyielding work ethic taught her
that hard work was the secret to success, and a brilliant mother
who, Presnell says proudly, "writes amazingly well."

Most importantly, "I was never told I couldn't accomplish
something. If anything, my dad would always tell me, 'You

can do *everything.*'" She believes this upbringing allowed her to pursue exciting adventures and experiences throughout her life.

Her father's life lesson resonated as Presnell explored her career choices. One of the first jobs in which she found great joy was her participation in search-and-rescue missions with the National Ski Patrol. She assumed her natural next step was a career in nursing, "But when I was done with nursing school, I realized that some parts of it—the charts and shots, the blood pressure taking, the rounds—weren't really for me. I knew I needed more excitement." She decided to return to school and earned a Bachelor's Degree in Business.

After graduation, Presnell, like many students who enjoyed their college environment, found a job at the school's admissions office. Although she enjoyed it, her wanderlust soon returned. "I enjoyed talking with prospective students about their future in college, making choices about studies whichthat would influence future choices for their careers," she says. "But I couldn't stop wondering what it was that I really wanted to do with my life. I knew it was time for another career change."

UNEXPECTEDLY FINDING HER LIFE'S WORK IN NUCLEAR ENERGY

Presnell soon found a much better fit—one that turned into a life-long career—quite by accident. She remembers it well. She had friends in Northern Idaho who worked in the nuclear industry. "I was twenty-seven or twenty-eight years old at the time. One night, I was enjoying a conversation with friends who were radiation-protection technicians. Over wine, one of my friends said, 'Well, you know, we could get you a job at Diablo Canyon in Central California as a Junior RP (radiation-protection) tech if you like.'"

Her friends went into more detail, telling her about the job and assuring her that she would be able to pass the qualification test. "You could give it a try and then take the summer off to figure out what direction you'd like to go with your career," they told her.

"We all laughed and I agreed. It sounded so dreamy and wonderful, the way ideas that are really 'out there' capture your attention and just don't let go," Presnell recalls. When she went back to her admissions job, she couldn't stop thinking about the opportunity her friends had described and soon Presnell was on the move once more. Excited by the chance to try something she thought she'd really love, Presnell went back to her friends, still not believing this dream would actually happen. She blurted out to them, "'If you can get me a job, I'm going to do it!' And they did it! They got me a job!"

A PRODUCTIVE, LUCRATIVE, AND HAPPY CAREER CHOICE

Presnell received an offer from Diablo Canyon which was then operated by Pacific Gas and Electric (PGE). She learned she would be working during the refueling "outages," during which the power plant was shut down for maintenance, repairs, and the replacement of spent fuel with new fuel. These types of evolutions take place at the over ninety nuclear power plants around the United States. The wages were generous and when Presnell considered the overtime on top of the base, it added up to quite a bit of money in a short time. She recalls that the income was a pleasant surprise, but other rewards of her new job were what hooked her for life.

So what exactly does a radiation-protection tech do? The position—along with instrumentation control technicians, electricians, pipe fitters, boiler makers, iron workers, and other technical experts—make up the required nuclear contract workers who "staff outages" at nuclear power plants. A radiation protection technician performs tasks such as checking for contamination levels and handling a Masslin mop (a mop of oil-treated cloth, swept in large, "S" movements along the floor). Presnell points out, "It's something that's relatively simple, but you must master reading instruments that measure radiation levels."

According to Presnell, "Maintaining nuclear power plants is like trying to keep a 1950s car on the road." These plants are continually aging; they were never designed to run the thirty-plus years that they've been in service. During her early career, all power plants were getting twenty-year extensions because no new plants were being built.

Every eighteen to twenty-four months, equipment (such as the boiler reactor or a pressure reactor) has to be shut down and refilled. This is called an "outage," and the required work to make repairs and bring in new fuel is known as "refueling." When plants shut down to refuel, it takes a small army of qualified people to repair anything which requires maintenance. At the same time, Operations and Engineering must replace the spent fuel from within the core with new fuel. This process of bundling tasks during scheduled outages is part of a strategy to keep plants from having to shut down from time to time for minor repairs.

"We have to keep these old power plants running safely until new technology becomes licensed, something the industry is currently in the process of doing," Presnell explains. But she notes we are actually behind in building new technology here in the United States, and there are quite a few other countries using these new technologies in their nuclear power generation programs already.

She realizes the challenge, "We haven't been able to implement new technologies due, in part, to negative public opinion. It's really held us up." She believes people in the U.S. don't understand that nuclear power is a remarkably clean source of energy—something she feels is at the heart of a vital public education challenge for the industry.

"When you're working on an outage, you put in a lot of hours in a short period of time. You work seventy-two hours a week— six twelve-hour-shifts, either day or night," Presnell remembers. "But you know you're sucking it up for the short term to have a lot of free time. More importantly, you're keeping the power on and making sure the plant's workers and its neighbors are safe."

Presnell was told, and ultimately learned for herself, that there is a wonderful kindred spirit and sense of community among the technicians working an outage. People in the same circuit work on the same outages and look out for each other. She knows it's a unique lifestyle, and she also knows it's made her very happy.

Presnell recalls when she first went to the Diablo Canyon power plant in California for two weeks of training and testing. The whole process fascinated her. "The learning curve was just huge! There was so much to learn and so much to absorb. But it was a lot of fun and the people there really enjoy what they do."

Presnell was a radiation-protection technician for thirteen years, working all over the United States at different nuclear power plants. During those years, she moved up from the lowest-level person onsite to an ANSI 3.1 level professional. And she had a great time. "You have a plethora of people out there and they're like gypsies. The people who work these outages, they work circuits, they work for different contract companies, they work six to eight months out of a year. In return, they generally have the summers off, plus another month in the winter. I lived this life for many years, and it was a wonderful life."

The excellent wages afforded her opportunities that, as a young person, she otherwise would never have had the chance to take advantage of. For example, in the early days of her career, she spent quite a bit of time in her Diablo Canyon position. After working her second outage there, she had saved up enough money to take three months off and backpack through Central America. Presnell remembers this period of her life with fondness, "Every time I went and worked an outage, I would take a different route back home across the country. One time I went exploring every park in Southern Utah—Zion, Bryce, Canyon Lands, and Arches. I love backpacking and I love hot springs, so I would hit every hot spring I could find on the way home."

The money she earned also allowed her to fulfill a dream – she bought eleven acres in northern Idaho and built her dream cabin. For six years, Presnell worked a year at a time on the circuit, then returned to the cabin and upgraded the property— drilling a well, improving the landscape, and grading the road. Though she now lives in Washington State, she still has her cabin and acreage. She goes there as often as possible.

Presnell notes building a dream home isn't unusual among her peers. "There are lots of people who do it. They travel regularly to keep our nuclear power plants operating safely. Then they come home and build their houses. They're able to do it without taking out loans or without waiting years, because they make a lot of money at one time." Their skill, their craft, and their technical knowledge afford them flexible, financially rewarding lifestyles.

She has a lot of respect and fondness for her colleagues. "In our field, there are lots of free spirits—a lot of interesting characters, free-thinking, bright, and intelligent people. It's a really great way to make a living."

Presnell wants people to understand while the pay for RP techs is high there is also a lot of accompanying responsibility. Ensuring the safety of a nuclear power plant when there is some sort of outage is demanding and sometimes challenging work, but Presnell points out that the work also calls for creative thinking to solve problems. "It challenges you on a lot of different levels," she says. "To this day, fourteen years later, I still learn something new every time I get to a new power plant, whether it's unfamiliar technology or a new system of one kind or another. I think that fact keeps a lot of people here for the long haul."

TRAINING AS A RADIATION-PROTECTION TECHNICIAN
Back in "the early days," people interested in entering the field had to study on their own. Programs like the Nuclear Technology Program at Columbia Generating Station, which Presnell was instrumental in establishing, didn't exist. Prospects either came out of the Nuclear Power School run by the Navy in Goose Creek, South Carolina, or were the kind of people who had the ability to learn on their own, with the aptitude and drive to assimilate all the information required to pass the qualification test needed to work as a technician in a nuclear plant.

Today, students in a two-year degree are being taught what Presnell learned in a few weeks of training, plus some information she studied voluntarily. Students in this program have to pass the national Northeast Utilities exams at the end of their studies to qualify as a radiation-protection technician. Of course, Presnell had to pass the test without the advantage of two years of classroom training.

Presnell is rightfully proud of her independent accomplishments, but she realizes prospective RP techs just can't do it on their own anymore. The industry is growing and accidents such as 1986's Chernobyl and 2011's Fukushima have brought to the forefront the need for increased safety. The Nuclear Regulatory Commission has stepped up by implementing ever-improving safety measures to prevent or effectively manage similar accidents, if and when they should occur.

Although the job of radiation-protection tech is overall a safe one, there is always the possibility that someone might be exposed to high levels of radiation. Presnell remembers one particular incident that occurred when she was a new senior tech. "Being a senior tech meant I could do my job independently. I was working at DC Cook (a nuclear power plant located just north of the city of Bridgman, Michigan). They needed to replace the baffle bolts in the plant's core barrel. It was extremely challenging work." In fact, the plant managers had to bring in an elite team from Germany with the specialized equipment required to remove these bolts and replace them.

Presnell was a bit surprised that the team from Germany "was a bit more lax than you'd expect, or want. I decided to watch them pretty closely. They were doing things the way they did in Germany, which is a little different than how we did things here."

In the U.S., there are strict NRC guidelines for how technicians cover jobs and what they can be exposed to. In this particular case, the German team had the necessary underwater equipment (used because water provides excellent shielding for radiation). Using underwater handheld tools, they were taking out the old bolts and putting them in a basket. Presnell explains what happened next, "They thought they had taken all the bolts out, and they were bringing up the basket to put another piece of equipment in it. There is a rule that requires me to check the radiation dose rates down in the water with an instrument called an 'amp 100' before things could continue, but they were pulling the basket up without getting it to me first. I shouted, 'Wait! Hold it. Stop! Let me come and check this.' I was basically chewing them out."

She checked the 'amp 100' and it was reading 3 rem, which is an alarming radiation level. They had not noticed a piece of broken bolt that was in the corner of the basket. If they had continued pulling it up, the team would have received a dangerously high dose of radiation.

Having a good rapport with colleagues is almost as important as good technical training, Presnell points out. "When I was new and inexperienced, I couldn't have gotten through without people showing me the importance of knowing what to watch for, knowing when to check, controlling the jobs, and, most important, working well with other people." She stresses that workers need to have good social skill sets to succeed. An outage at a power plant requires working with all types of work groups, and every one of them has to work as a team to ensure the components are reassembled safely, refueled, and put back online.

As with any group of people working together, there may be conflicts, circumstances when it's hard to stay on schedule and get things done. But time is of the essence; situations can worsen quite suddenly – things get broken and new mechanical issues are discovered. She warns, "It can get dangerous really fast. It's really important that you have the social skills and technical knowledge to fix a bad situation and get everyone back working on the same goal."

THE NEED FOR A NEW GENERATION OF NUCLEAR TECHS

Presnell emphasizes the pressing need to get more techs trained in the nuclear field. The current generation of RP technicians is largely made up of baby boomers, who are retiring at an accelerating rate. With younger colleagues in short supply, many techs are leaving without passing along to others their knowledge and skills. Says Presnell, "In my thirteen years as a radiation tech, I worked outages all over the country and saw firsthand the attrition issues we have with the 102 commercial nuclear power plants now in service. We must educate the next generation."

That is best accomplished first in the classroom and then in the power plants with on-the-job training.

Not preparing the next generation of RP techs, she believes, is irresponsible. "The people who have been doing this for the last thirty years are the ones who used to come in, take you by the hand, and show you how contamination travels and teach you how to control it. They'd say, 'When you take these valves apart, you have to be able to know to take your smears into check, and this is how you need to address people,'" she remembers her mentors telling her, "We need to keep that knowledge alive."

Presnell notes without that knowledge transfer, she would never have learned all the ins and outs of the nuclear industry. She emphasizes this in-depth, practical knowledge is not something you can learn in a book. These technical positions are hands-on. Yes, students must understand the theoretical science behind nuclear power, but without getting the experience from the people who have been working with it for years, the next generation will have major gaps in knowledge.

Ensuring the next generation of technicians will be well prepared through knowledge transferred from the current generation of techs is a goal of the Nuclear Technology Program at Columbia Generating Station in Washington. Not surprisingly, this program is coordinated by Presnell.

She first learned of the program from Charlie McDonald, a nuclear worker who wanted to start a program in partnership with Columbia Basin College. It was part of a national movement the Nuclear Energy Institute (NEI) and the Institute of Nuclear Power Operations (INPO) had begun in an attempt to recruit and train the next generation. The program was "something that really got me interested in solving a new problem, something different and important at this stage of my career."

When McDonald began looking for someone to work with the college and build the program, Presnell was one of the few people he had met who had actually worked as one of these technicians. She immediately agreed it was worth getting off the road as an outage team member to become part of the venture. Once she began actively working with the program, she and her colleagues worked alongside INPO, NEI, and the Regional Center for Nuclear Education and Training (RCNET).

Presnell remains passionate about the importance of transferring knowledge from the current generation to the next generation. "It's really taken a huge cultural shift in the mind-set of people to accept these programs as part of our work and to understand how important our work is in order for the industry to keep moving forward. We're doing that, and it's exciting to see."

In her work to shape the program, Presnell brought a different perspective than many other educators. Academic education was of course essential, but again, the key was transferring the hands-on technical experience that would make the program effective. Just because these programs were training students to work in a nuclear power plant didn't answer Presnell's question, "How the heck do we get them in the door of the plant?"

She realized that unless the students could safely perform the hands-on technical tasks, they wouldn't be able to do the job when they were most needed. Presnell saw this as a barrier which some of her colleagues simply had missed, "So, from the get-go, I kept aggressively pushing the fact that we're never going to get nuclear power plants to hire these students unless we give them actual on-the-job training with industry experts, along with certifications and qualifications."

Presnell advocated for paid internships for the students, taking meetings with senior management to get the decision-makers on board. She made the case that every student from her program must complete an internship in order to graduate. Presnell further insisted it was the industry's responsibility to fund these internships. Ultimately, not all of these internships were paid, but those fortunate enough to get internships through Energy Northwest went through the program at no cost to them. The addition of the internship requirement helped to quiet some of the incumbent techs who complained the students wouldn't know what they were doing in the real world. "You're right!" Presnell told the dubious incumbent techs. "They won't know. It's your job to show them. When people are new in any business, they're complete novices. Remember, you were once a novice, too."

The importance of apprenticeships is essential for qualifying plumbers and electricians, among other trades. Yet until recently, there wasn't anything like that in the nuclear industry. "In the early days, everything in nuclear was kind of unofficial," she says. "Somebody got a job for their friend, their brother, or their child. Like me, if you remember. There never was even any type of official training program. It was all kind of willy-nilly." Fortunately, the one thing in place to weed people out was the requirement to pass official exams. If an applicant didn't have the aptitude, he or she wouldn't pass.

While in the past, fellow employees would take the time to make sure "rookies" were properly trained, in today's larger industry, it's no longer possible to rely upon these informal systems. Presnell points out that the small amount of money it takes to create these internships for the next generation will ensure the transfer of practical knowledge and keep power plants operating safely.

Another topic she pushed for at the beginning was teaching new techs the history of nuclear power, "But not from a dates and facts approach," Presnell points out. She felt they were missing an opportunity for current workers to relate the history of nuclear power to the next generation. "I told everyone we really need to get our stories down and talk about the history of how we got into this industry, how the industry evolved, and our place in that world, because, if not, we're going to lose that perspective when the current generation retires. Many people are in their sixties now and they're leaving. We need to capture their stories before they go."

Presnell is also passionate about getting labs established within the training programs—not just for her own program, but for all the colleges offering nuclear technician training—so students can practice their craft and hone their skills in a safe environment, without the danger of a radiation dose. "They need to learn how to take apart an air-operated valve in a safe environment," she emphasizes.

Another thing most programs now recognize is the need to provide certificates and certifications that will help students get hired and become trusted employees in nuclear facilities.

There's also been a movement to add on-the-job (OJT) training and training performance evaluations (TPE), and to make OJT and TPE requirements identical for all nuclear power plants. This is one way to assure students are knowledgeable and proficient at required tasks. Bringing that consistency to the labs and actually qualifying students in the National PED's database, makes the students transferable and employable, not only at one facility, but at any other nuclear facility in the country.

Another concern is the number of jobs that will be available. Presnell noted, "These programs can't sustain on nuclear power alone. Nuclear power is not going to be able to hire every graduate from this program." She recognized the curriculum needed to expand to other types of energy and safety issues. She pushed educators to recognize they must make graduates not only valuable to nuclear utilities but other industries as well. She says, "Hiring man-

agers are reluctant to hire inexperienced graduates from many programs. It requires a lot of time and money resources until graduates
from these programs can work independently."

Presnell looks positively to the future. "Nuclear Power is a
business that has to remain fiscally solvent. However, waiting
until the baby boomers have retired leaves a huge gap in knowledge transfer. This loss of knowledge transfer is what I am so pas-
sionately trying to mitigate. Everything needs its checks and
balances. Nuclear must put its checks in the box to remain fiscally viable for generations to come, and my goal is to balance
that check in the box by ensuring the next generation receives
the knowledge transfer and is well educated to continue the safe
operation of our nuclear power plants."

The Nuclear Technology Program that Presnell coordinates
takes place in the evenings so it can attract those instructors who
spend most days at work. Presnell notes they are fortunate to be
located in Richland, Washington, because it is, as she puts it, "a
very nuclear community."

The program boasts instructors from the Hanford Site (a
mostly decommissioned nuclear production complex), AREVA
(a world leader in nuclear power), the Pacific Northwest National
Laboratory, and Washington River Protection Solutions (preem-
inent nuclear waste management contractors), as well as licensed
operators, instrumentation control technicians, radiation-protection technicians, and chemistry professionals from the public
power joint operating agency, Energy Northwest.

The instructors bring thirty years of personal operating experience to the program. This gives them a great deal of expertise
to support the knowledge transfer Presnell is so passionate about.
She is proud of these accomplished, experienced people who not
only understand the theory but also possess the practical skills
that come from actually operating a nuclear power plant.

From the beginning, the NRC has provided copious amounts of grant money for the program. "None of our programs would be up and going without the Nuclear Regulatory Commission," Presnell says. Most of these programs started with NRC grant money, combined with partnerships between utilities and local colleges. Grant money continues to be vital, providing operating funds as well as the required equipment.

In Presnell's program, once students complete their in-class training and internships, they must pass required tests for the jobs for which they are training. For example, RP techs are required to pass the radiation fundamentals national exam, which must be repeated and passed every five years. Operators must also take an aptitude test called the Plant Operator Selection System (POSS) exam.

Students must pass these exams and be officially qualified before they leave her program. Their success is then recorded in the national database; a valuable tool in helping graduates get hired. Other educational programs are now implementing this level of testing as well.

Presnell's program is now starting to place graduates in industry positions. "Three equipment operators who just went through our first non-license operator program at Energy Northwest were hired by our power plant a little over a year ago. They all took the equipment operator class and they're now working in those positions here. It's very rewarding. But it's just a start."

These are exciting times for Presnell, because it was hard to convince the "old Navy Nuclear guys" that a degree from her program would actually educate new recruits up to their standards. When the three new hires from Presnell's program began their work, Energy Northwest also hired an additional twelve equipment operators from Navy Nuclear. "It was really great because, not only did our kids do as well as the Navy Nuclear hires; they actually outscored them in two areas of study It was rewarding that the older generation was able to see we're doing the right things with our Nuclear Technology Program. We're educating them to the rigorous standards we need them to have. The supervisors, who are responsible for the newly hired graduates, are really happy with our students' performance. Further, our Instrumentation and Control Department just hired three more graduates from our program into an In-Grade position, whereby they will work this next year towards acquiring their phase-one qualifications, allowing them to work independently on a specific task."

The students from the program also seem to love it. Presnell reports, "There's so much to learn, the systems are so complicated and the science behind how the reactors work creating energy from neutron bombarding is fascinating. They are amazed, thinking, 'Wow, this is how the science really works.' When I walk into Columbia Basin College to conduct an observation, when I work with the great people who manage the day-to-day operation of the degree program, the students always approach me to discuss some exciting new topic and to ask more questions. Those are the days I feel the best about what we're doing."

Energy Northwest remains pleased with the graduates from Presnell's program. The company recently hired four more graduates as technicians for its Instrumentation and Control shop. But Presnell notes it isn't all sunshine, and a huge cultural issue remains. "A lot of the older baby-boomer generation doesn't want to let the new generation come in, saying, 'They don't know.'" Presnell agrees, but she never fails to challenge them. "That's why we need to get them in so you can share with them your years of experience. Because, guess what? You're not going to be here forever."

LESSONS LEARNED

■ Nuclear technicians earn great benefits in a short amount of time. The workload can be heavy and intense, because techs shoulder a lot of responsibility to make sure everyone is safe.

■ Communication is paramount. Technicians have to communicate effectively at all levels.

■ The accumulated knowledge of the retiring workers needs to be transferred to the new incoming workers.

■ Training is vital. Classroom settings have to be complemented with hands-on internships, simulations, and other affective domain training methods to ensure a well-rounded education.

CHAPTER 3

◆

JOHN TASCHNER

Lt. Col., US Air Force (Ret.)

One of the things we found out later on, that we didn't know
during the Cuban Missile Crisis, was that the Soviets had sent
four diesel submarines to Cuba, and they were armed with
nuclear torpedoes. It's a good thing we didn't know about that.

WHEN JOHN TASCHNER GRADUATED FROM SAN JOSE STATE COLLEGE WITH
a degree in medical technology in 1954, he knew he would soon
be drafted into the military. He took the initiative, "I wrote to the
Air Force Surgeon General, told him I'd be coming out with a
degree in hospital laboratory sciences and 'I would like to enlist
[in the Air Force]' if I can use that as a starting point for my
career. The Air Force wrote back and said, 'Come on board, son.'"

Thus began a long and prestigious career. After three years
of teaching lab sciences at Gunter Air Force Base, the medical

service school in Montgomery, Alabama, the Air Force sent Taschner to Washington, D.C., to take courses in their new nuclear medicine program. "About halfway through that program, a colonel for the surgeon general called me up and said we needed to talk about my next assignment."

The Air Force was setting up a health physics laboratory in Dayton, Ohio, and they needed to train three officers within a year to staff it. The surgeon general told me, 'We want to send you to Los Alamos to get your training in health physics.'" Taschner's response was, "What's health physics?"

DEVELOPING SAFETY PROCEDURES

The Air Force explained health physics was a discipline that was born out of the Manhattan Project; its goal was to study effects of radiation on people and to use this knowledge to develop radiation safety procedures. It sounded good to Taschner.

So, here he was in 1958, heading to Los Alamos for training in a new field. "That was awesome. I had just gotten married and my wife and I drove about 2,000 miles from Washington, D.C., to Los Alamos. I reported in there on a Monday morning. My boss, Health Director Tom Shipman, told me to get our stuff moved in to our new apartment because on Wednesday I was going to the Nevada test site for a month on nuclear weapons testing. I said, 'Oh, boy!'"

Taschner spent thirty days in Nevada where the last aboveground nuclear weapons tests were taking place. On the final day of October, just before midnight, the final shot was fired. "They were trying to test everything they could. About half were called 'safety shots,' where not all the detonators in the weapon were hooked together. This was done to simulate what might happen if a bomber crashed or there was some other type of accident. Would the shockwave detonate the weapon and would it go nuclear?" The other test shots were actual nuclear shots

"We were doing radiation monitoring. The weapons were tethered from balloons about 200 feet in the air. There were bunkers on the ground some distance away from ground zero that contained radiation-sensitive experiments and high-speed cameras. The bunkers had big steel doors secured with large hex nuts. You needed to get to ground zero as soon as you could to recover the film before it fogged. So, two of us health physicists, one driving, the other one sitting in the back seat hanging out the window would go into the bunkers. We were all wearing personal protective apparel with full-face respirators. The bunkers' big steel doors faced away from the blast. We'd get there, spin off the big hex nuts with a speed wrench, while the driver called the technicians in to do what they needed to do, and then we'd leave as fast as we could!

"Radiation safety equipment has evolved since 1958; it is now much more sensitive, but it still isn't all that different. When discussing contamination, we always talk about things that were twice background [twice the normal background levels]. If it reads so many counts per minute, or twice background, it was said to be contaminated. The number keeps going down because of the increased sensitivity of the instruments. But the equipment itself is pretty much the same, though a little bit smaller," says Taschner. "Most of the instruments in those days had big batteries on them; now they're all kind of like flashlight batteries." So, although the technology has gotten more sensitive and utilizes more modern electronics, today's technicians are measuring contamination areas using basically the same equipment Taschner used back in '58.

A moratorium on nuclear testing in the United States began on that last day of October 1958, so Taschner returned to Los

Alamos and began his health physics training. He was reassigned from one group to another on "the hill," as they call it, learning everything he could about radiation safety procedures and the effects of radiation on human health. He studied particle accelerators on a small reactor, worked in the tritium processing plant, and spent time where plutonium pits for nuclear weapons were fabricated.

He was moved from place to place in order to get a broader background on all aspects of health physics. "Shipman would assign me to a place, and then every Friday afternoon I would meet with him and talk about what I had learned. He'd say, 'OK, that's enough,' then call somebody and tell them this wet-be-hind-the-ears lieutenant (who would be me) would be knocking on their door Monday morning. So I was off to someplace else."

All this training was in anticipation of joining the health physics laboratory in Ohio, but the original order for three people to join was lowered to two and Taschner ended up the odd man out. En route to Ohio, his orders changed. "I was a critical laboratory officer and they needed someone with my credentials at what they called the epidemiological laboratory over at Lackland Air Force Base. It wasn't a pleasant surprise for me. I wound up staying there for two years, which I hated because I wanted to be in health physics. I had completed all that fantastic training and they had sent me back to where I started."

Frustrated, Taschner considered leaving the Air Force. "I didn't really want to, but I received a job offer from the Atomic Energy Commission. I talked to my colonel and said, 'Look, apparently you don't have an interest in me being a health physicist, so I'm going to leave the Air Force.' He really got serious, finally found me a job back down at Gunter Air Force Base, this time as a health physicist teaching nuclear weapons effects to Air Force medical service corps personnel."

THE CUBAN MISSILE CRISIS

He was still teaching at Gunter in October 1962 at the advent of the Cuban Missile Crisis. Since he and his colleagues were considered experts in the effects of nuclear weapons, they were called on to help educate officers at Maxwell Air Force Base, which was right across town. "We supplied our expertise to the command post there when they had war games, simulating the effects of nuclear weapons detonations. We would do fallout predictions and damage assessments as our part of the games." Since this was long before computer modeling came into the picture, his team had to display their predictions using basic graphs.

"When the Cuban Missile Crisis occurred, we were training a lot of people about survival in a nuclear attack. We thought we were going to go to war. We were over there [at Maxwell] for briefings and things were really looking bad. One morning, I went to teach a two-hour course, and, as soon as I finished my lecture, I was told to get my butt over to the command post. When I walked out the door, I told the secretary to call my wife and tell her I wouldn't be home for dinner.

"I finally got home – three days later. I had been saddled up in a command post, thinking and listening, hearing briefings about what was going on during the crisis. It was tense. Nobody was panicking; we were just doing our job, but we were quite concerned this situation was going to go nuclear.' His teaching went quickly from academics to reality. "All of a sudden, you think, my God, we're really going to do this."

Still, Taschner remained levelheaded. "We were well-trained, we knew what we had to do, and we were ready. We had practiced in a number of war games that went nuclear. So we were just sitting there waiting for something to happen so we'd be able to go and do what we had to do."

"One of the things we found out later on, that we didn't know during the Cuban Missile Crisis, was that the Soviets had sent four diesel submarines to Cuba, and they were armed with nuclear torpedoes. It's a good thing we didn't know about that. You may know the story – there were four subs, and each one had its own commander, but there was a flotilla commander in one of the submarines. The submarine he was in was the one an American destroyer finally was able to get to surface. The commander of the submarine wanted to fire the nuclear torpedoes, but the flotilla commander said, 'We're not going to do that.' There was a movie about him, *The Man Who Saved the World*. Had he ordered the nuclear torpedoes to be fired, we would almost certainly have been in a nuclear war with the Soviet Union.

WORKING WITH NASA

After assisting with the national crisis, Taschner returned to teaching. Shortly after, his boss noted Taschner didn't have a master's degree. "I said there probably isn't a college in the country that would accept me for a graduate program. And he said, 'Wrong, you're going to school in September,'" Taschner remembers. "So, in September, 1964, my family and I moved to Lawrence, Kansas, where I went to the University of Kansas for two years and got a master's degree in radiation biophysics." Though this was all paid for by the Air Force, Taschner recalls, "I was just a student, no other responsibilities. I dressed like a civilian for two years."

After receiving his degree, Taschner moved on to Wright-Patterson Air Force Base in Ohio, where he had originally thought he'd be stationed after his Los Alamos training.

"I thought I was going to be running the Air Force's 'personal dosimetry program,'" Taschner says. "The program processed and monitored about a quarter-million film badges [which measure the wearer's radiation level] worn by Air Force personnel all over the world. But they had a vacancy in the bio-assay and analytical chemistry group and my boss put me in charge there instead."

Taschner says he was the world's worst chemist, put in charge of doing some rather sophisticated chemistry—including measuring plutonium levels in the urine of Air Force personnel involved in a nuclear accident in Palomares, Spain, in January of 1966.

They had 400 samples from this accident in which a B-52 Strategic Air Command bomber collided with a KC-135 tanker during mid-air refueling. The bomber had four Mk28-type hydrogen bombs on board and the accident resulted in the release of plutonium, which contaminated about 640 acres. "When I got there I found that the analytical procedures at the Radiological Health Laboratory didn't work. My boss said, 'This is your job, and by the way, the people you're going to command don't know how to do it.'"

As luck would have it, Taschner had gone to a symposium on bio-essay and analytical chemistry. "And a guy named Warren Shien from Mountain Laboratory, just twenty miles south of me, had reported on this new, sophisticated method of doing a precise analysis of adult human urine. I had his business card, so I called him up, said I needed help, and went down to see him. I told him our problem, and he and his technician came up and spent a whole week with us. They brought some of their equipment and some of the chemicals, and they trained my staff and me how to use their method. Within a week, we were on a production schedule, working two eight-hour shifts a day, processing samples, and achieving exquisite results. It just goes to show, it isn't what you know, it's who you know, and I have one hell of an address book!"

While Taschner was at Wright-Patterson, Colonel Lionel Arnoldi retired from the Air Force and went to work at NASA. He and his chief health physicist were looking over their health physics programs, and they were finding gaps that needed to be addressed. They were concerned that they were going to have to rewrite a number of contracts to get this done, when Colonel Arnoldi suddenly realized he knew who could solve the problem.

As Taschner explains, "The Colonel said he had had a laboratory under his command at Wright-Patterson with a bunch of health physicists, and we knew we could get it done. So NASA funded our radiological health lab to do all of its radiation safety work, and that job fell to me."

By and large, the NASA projects were primarily the same as the ones Taschner was conducting for the Air Force, such as measuring radiation from x-ray machines and industrial radiography equipment. But NASA also needed support for all of its Apollo launches. "There was what they called a SNAP 27 device that was attached to the Lunar Module," explains Taschner. "It was filled with an isotope called plutonium 238, which was a heat source. Basically, you took it out and put it into a generator, which converted the nuclear heat to electrical power, providing about 60 watts of DC power for the lunar experiments they had planned. If there was a catastrophic problem and something happened to the missile on the pad, there was a minute chance the source might be ruptured. If it did, plutonium would scatter all over the Cape and surrounding areas. So I would take a team of about eight or ten technicians and young officers down there to prepare to do air sampling and field monitoring to detect plutonium contamination."

A SHORT RETIREMENT

Taschner was transferred to Germany in June 1970, to be the health physicist for the United States Air Force in Europe, but continued to provide support to NASA for the Apollo launches, flying back to Cape Kennedy when needed.

"When I went to Germany, I was a major. I got promoted to lieutenant colonel during my last year in Europe, and normally when you get promoted, you have a two- year obligation. So I was finishing up my last year in Europe, expecting an assignment back to the United States to finish off my last year, and then the Air Force said, 'Well, you can go home now. Thank you for your service.' Of course, I was not happy about their decision, but there was nothing I could do about it."

So Taschner sent his family to California to be with his parents, went back to McGuire Air Force Base in New Jersey to be retired, picked up his final paycheck, and separated from the service on July 1, 1974, after twenty-one years. "All in all, it was a great career," he remembers.

With his experience, he wasn't retired for long. According to Taschner, "The Public Health Service Admiral who was the director of the United States Public Health Service (USPHS) Bureau of Radiological Health in Rockville, Maryland, hired me as a staff member in their Standards and Regulations Branch. My job was to write performance standards for diagnostic x-ray equipment. But, while I was there, Three Mile Island happened."

Taschner expounded on his role during the incident and the follow-up. "When the partial meltdown occurred on March 29, 1979, a group called the TMI group was formed with five senior health physicists to support all the public health service efforts at the site. We had an office at the State of Pennsylvania Radiological Control Program Office and we were just trying to help the state in the radiological issues of Three Mile Island. We actually were part of the Food and Drug Administration, so there were several FDA people who went to TMI to sample milk and other materials around the island. Those samples were all sent to a place in Massachusetts for analysis. I helped to coordinate those efforts, working with other Federal agencies to coordinate sampling programs. I got there just after the initial incident and worked out of a trailer just outside the reactor building itself."

The environmental sampling programs were extensive, and, of course, there was the chaos caused by the news media and government agencies that descended on the sleepy Pennsylvania countryside. "Everyone was collecting milk from all the dairies in the area as well as many other types of samples," Taschner recalls. "The TMI Plant, the state, the EPA, the USPHS, and others were all collecting samples. It seemed like all of the milk from all of the dairy farms in the area was in someone's laboratory being analyzed for radioactivity. But we didn't find anything. And we didn't think we would, because it was a time of the year most cattle were on stored feed; they weren't grazing. And iodine has a short half-life before it dies, so it goes away pretty fast. Ultimately, the exposures up there were really trivial."

Still, Taschner was sympathetic to the concerns of the public. "You don't realize how scary something like this is while it's going on. There was real concern that hydrogen might be building up in the reactor, and with the radiation and heat, people thought it could explode, blow the core. A lot of fears turned out not to be true, but they still created a lot of panic. This had never happened before, and we saw firsthand how powerful fear of the unknown can be."

The amount of work and research Taschner and his colleagues did is astounding when you realize they weren't using computerized tools. "Most of my time was spent at my desk, helping the state get resources that they might need, or getting people up there to do milk or air sampling. We had a meeting about every day to share survey estimates and information." It's interesting that TMI is also short for too much information. Taschner remembers how hectic things could get. "We would come in with a survey, other agencies would give us theirs, and sometimes it turned out our stuff was the same as what they gave us yesterday, and vice versa. We had a pile of data—all of it on paper—that just went up, up, up exponentially. It was difficult to sort it all out."

NAVY DEPUTY DIRECTOR

Taschner stayed at the Bureau of Radiological Health until 1983. At that point, the Navy was looking for a deputy director of their nuclear weapons radiological control program. The Navy had a unique problem: their sailors slept and worked in close proximity to nuclear weapon storage spaces aboard ships, and nuclear weapons emit low levels of gamma and neutron radiation. However, the surveys, which were done on board ships that carried nuclear weapons, primarily aircraft carriers, found that these radiation levels, although small, could gradually build up. Over time, particularly on long deployments, the crew's exposure could possibly exceed the Navy's established permissible limits. The Naval Sea Systems Command created a unit to solve this problem, and Taschner was back in the armed forces as its Deputy Director.

Taschner remembers this time fondly.

"Working for the Navy was a great job. We had a unit down in Yorktown, Virginia, that did a lot of our fieldwork overseeing radiation safety programs at naval bases. Then we had a group at headquarters that was primarily responsible for nuclear weapons safety. So I had the responsibility of leading two units of really great people. I often asked myself, should I lead, or follow? I was never quite sure since all of them were dedicated people and did their jobs very well."

In order to protect sailors from exposure from weapons within their proximity, Taschner's team put shielding, or a physics package, around the weapons themselves. "We got a nice accolade from Admiral Watkins, the Chief of Naval Operations, for our work. It was an exciting time."

On January 1, 1990, Taschner's wife, Beth, died. They had been married for thirty-two years and she was only fifty-five years old. The couple had two children, Robert and Karen. Taschner remembers, "It was a great loss to all of us. She weathered the storm of many changes of Air Force assignments in my early career, and my frequent travels. There were a lot of ups and downs. Losing Beth was a great loss for my children and me."

Early in Taschner's ninth year of working for the Navy, "President Bush and the Navy decided in 1992 they were going to take nuclear weapons off of every vessel except submarines," recalls Taschner. "Because of this decision, the most challenging part of my job went away. Looking around, I could see what was going to happen next, and I knew that my job was going to be downgraded sooner or later. So, a few months later, in September of 1992, I ended up where I started by getting a job back at Los Alamos National Laboratory, where I became a technical staff member assigned to the Hazardous Material Response Group."

He and another fellow from the Waste Implementation Pilot Plant (WIPP) in Carlsbad, New Mexico, were tasked with developing a course to train radiological assistant teams throughout the United States to respond to transportation accidents involving radioactive materials. This was the era when the U.S. started dealing with issues regarding the transportation of radioactive substances, determining whether the movement should be by train or trucks.

"We developed a curriculum and arranged for the instructors to teach the course. We also gave lectures ourselves," Taschner says. "We set up this program to train people how to respond to nuclear weapons accidents involving shipments of nuclear weapons' wastes from Department of Energy [DOE] facilities to the WIPP site."

He continues, "When I got there, they sent me up to Pocatello, Idaho, to observe what I was going to be doing. In one of the transportation exercises up there, they had three big cans on this truck filled with low-level plutonium waste. There were radiation warning signs on the side of each container stating the amount of nuclear material inside. I walked up to the signs and discovered there were only about 30 grams in each can. 'Good grief,' I thought, 'what are we doing here?' I had come out of the Navy, where I dealt with kilograms of plutonium in our safety programs. It was a whole new ball game."

Things had changed considerably from Taschner's early days in Los Alamos, when the protocol for responding to a nuclear weapon accident was pretty simple. "There was an outfit at Kirtland Air Force Base called JNACC, Joint Nuclear Accident Coordinating Center," he explains. "If an aircraft carrying a nuclear weapon crashed, the JNAAC would be notified. JNAAC would then call Los Alamos requesting assistance, since at that time; Los Alamos was the only designer of nuclear weapons. So a team from the Defense Nuclear Agency at Kirtland AFB and weapons design people from Los Alamos would hop on a plane and go to the accident site to assist in weapons recovery."

Taschner believes it is important for people to understand there wasn't much of a contamination issue in the early days. "In the early days, nuclear weapons were designed in what was called an 'open pit' configuration. The nuclear capsule part of the weapon (the part containing its radioactive material) was carried aboard the aircraft in a device called a 'bird cage.' It was never inserted into the weapon except in time of war. Therefore, in an accident, plutonium contamination wouldn't occur, even if the conventional high explosives in the weapon detonated during the accident, because the plutonium was kept separate."

However, Taschner notes things have changed. "When they went to the new 'sealed pit' style of weapons, the plutonium core was now surrounded by high explosives and a bunch of detonators. The normal process would be to fire all the detonators at once, which would crush the plutonium from a subcritical mass to supercritical, creating a nuclear yield. In an accident situation, all those detonators don't go off at the same time, so there is no compression (implosion). Instead, the partial detonation of the weapon's explosives scatters the plutonium, creating a real contamination problem."

For example, Taschner points to the differences between the 1966 Palomares accident and the one at Thule Air Force Base in Greenland in 1968 involving a USAF B-52 bomber. In the Palomares accident, two high-explosive weapons detonated separately and contaminated a square mile of countryside. In the Thule accident, all four weapons on the aircraft, along with about 220,000 pounds of fuel on board, detonated simultaneously. But instead of spreading widely, a large portion of the plutonium became trapped in the burning jet fuel, limiting the contamination to an area of about one-sixteenth of a square mile.

Taschner's commitment to radiation safety spanned his entire career. He joined ANSI N43, a committee charged with codifying radiation safety standards for nonmedical equipment, when he was at the Radiological Health Laboratory in the 1960s. Eventually, he served as committee chair for over six years, remaining until the 1990s, when he returned to Los Alamos.

LIFE AFTER SERVICE

By the beginning of the new century, however, Taschner had had enough. "I was getting bored," he admits. "I didn't really want to leave, but the challenges weren't there anymore. I wanted more responsibility and I wanted to do the things I was qualified to do. You could pretty much hire a technician to do what my job required." So he and his second wife, Diana, found a place to retire. They ended up in Sparks, Nevada, near Reno. In October 2002, Taschner went to his boss and said he was quitting. He was now officially retired. Sadly, though, his second wife passed away recently.

As he continues to network with colleagues and committees, Taschner does have some concern about today's managers and how they lead their teams. He doesn't see the people who are coming up now gaining an understanding of how to take ownership of a project, moving it forward based on the existing parameters, and inspiring their teams to take ownership as well.

"It appears to me the people today are interested in being nine-to-fivers. They come to work in the morning, put their brains on, and shut them off when they leave," Taschner says. "People are just not interested in being involved in activities that support their career patterns. They don't seem to have the same level or standard of performance, responsibility, and accountability that we once had. I remember when I went to work for the Navy; I was told I had to take courses in leadership and management. I said, 'Okay, I've been doing this for thirty years, but I'll take your courses,' even though the guy who taught the course didn't have a clue about how to teach leadership. One Friday morning, when he came in the classroom, I said I had something to say. I got up and went to the blackboard, and I said, 'Lead as you would be led." Then I turned around and asked everyone in the room, 'What does that mean to you? Say you have a guy who has screwed up, how are you going to deal with him? Are you going to chew him out in front of everybody so everyone knows he really screwed up? Is that the way to lead people?

"No, take him in your office, sit down and talk about it, and find out why he made a mistake so it doesn't happen again. That's leading!' We built a team back in the Navy and everyone was a part of that team. Each person took responsibility for his part and held himself or herself accountable for the outcome. And we supported each other."

After a life spent training people in nuclear safety, Taschner also wants to make sure today's upcoming nuclear technicians understand the history of radiation safety standards, not just how but why they've evolved over the years. "It's good to know why. You know when procedures change, but it's always nice to know why they were written, why things were done *this* way before you change it to *that* way. That's one of the reasons I try to tell people a little bit about how radiation safety standards evolved over the years—to help them understand about why we are where we are, and how things moved forward."

Despite the tragedies in his life, Taschner looks back with a positive outlook. "Going to Los Alamos and learning the training there, and then going on to become a member of the Health Physics Society were the most magnificent things I ever did. I just got back from the HPS meeting in Indianapolis, where they honored me with a Founder's Award, their highest recognition for services in the field of health physics. It sure is nice to get a reward for having so much fun. Someone once said, 'If you love what you are doing, you will never work a day in your life.' That is what we all need to accomplish. I have. Now it's your turn."

LESSONS LEARNED

■ Technology and work processes are designed to ensure safety for those in the industry as well as the public.

■ Opportunities come from unexpected places. Be open to offers presented to you. It is important to enjoy the learning process, to be able to learn new skills and disciplines, and to be open to new ways of doing things as technology and methods evolve.

■ You cannot panic. You have to stay levelheaded, no matter the circumstances, to ensure no mistakes are made.

CHAPTER 4

◆

HAYDEN MERCER

Retired – Radiation Protection Technical Supervisor and Assistant Radiation-Protection Manager – Florida Power and Light Company

I firmly believe that, over the decades, the proactive nature of the nuclear industry has put us in a position to be able to make good, sound judgments about how we want to do business and how we want to operate our facilities. We've learned a lot along the way.

"HAVE YOU SEEN THE DODGE CAR COMMERCIAL THAT IS CURRENTLY ON television?" asks Hayden Mercer. "It features one of the new, high-performance cars. The front wheels are locked, the rear wheels are spinning, smoke is going up, and, if you look to the left side of the screen, you see an old 1914 model Dodge. To some extent, I think that's my analogy of where the nuclear industry started and where it is now."

Mercer looks back at the growth of the industry, noting that, as with any other technology, it started out with a glint of how to do something new, but needed real working experience to learn what required improvement and how to make those improvements. He believes that over time, the nuclear industry has grown by leaps and bounds into a highly sophisticated enterprise, a well-oiled machine.

Which is what reminds Mercer of that Dodge commercial. The nuclear industry's founders started with bare-bones equipment and technology. They knew the essentials – building circuits and building detectors to enable the measurement of radiation exposure. At that time, the instruments were constructed from vacuum tubes. Today, everything is computer-based.

Mercer holds up a pair of items. In his left hand, he grips a large slide rule and in his right hand, his smartphone. In his career, he explains, the slide rule was where he started, and the smartphone represents the technology of today. As the nuclear industry has grown, its tools have advanced. Technicians started with slide rules and adding machines, and now they utilize smartphones, which, despite their compact size, have as much computing power as the first computers used by NASA to put man on the moon.

The nuclear industry is one with many potential risks, all of which must first be understood and analyzed, and then well managed for the protection of the plant workers, the plant's neighbors, and the general public. "We've seen some of the effects, specifically in Chernobyl and Fukushima, of negative things that are physically possible with a nuclear facility," Mercer says.

While he realizes issues associated with nuclear accidents may worry the public, Mercer firmly believes the industry has learned important lessons over the decades, and that its proactive nature has put the industry in a position to make sound judgments based upon both real-life experience and theoretical understanding.

IN SEARCH OF A CAREER

Born and raised in West Texas as a rancher and a farmer, Mercer has been part of the industry for most of his adult life. After serving in Vietnam, where he was a Navy hospital corpsman when he realized he had little to look forward to. "I was kind of lost, along with so many others of my generation."

Stationed at the Naval Air Station Hospital in Corpus Christi, Texas, Mercer met a man who had come from the Navy's nuclear program. Until that time, the only Navy nuclear program Mercer knew of was its nuclear propulsion program—designed to power the submarines and aircraft carriers under the command of Admiral Rickover.

But it turned out there was an exclusive organization that was "tri-service"— Army, Navy, and Air Force. They maintained various small nuclear facilities, established to support the Distant Early Warning (DEW) line set up across Alaska, Greenland, Wyoming, and other remote locations, and designed to identify incoming Soviet missiles or aircraft engaged in an attack on the United States. They also operated a plant in Antarctica to provide power for the National Science Foundation and the Antarctic research program.

Mercer says, "This man told me he'd be retiring, and, once he told me about the Navy nuclear program, I thought I might like to work there, and decided to give it a shot." The Navy told him that, in order to be part of the program, he would have to reenlist for six years, pass both a psychological and physical exam, and take an aptitude test. If he passed the exams and was accepted, he would spend a year in training. He'd have no as-signments other than this training.

Then he'd spend thirteen months at McMurdo Station in Antarctica running a power plant. "I had to think about that a little bit," Mercer admits. "But I said, 'What the heck, how many people get to go to the South Pole?'"

THE VALUE OF PSYCHOLOGICAL TESTING
FOR STRESS SITUATIONS

Mercer agreed to give the Navy another six years, and took his physical and psychological tests. The psych tests were vital. Navy personnel who made it into the program would be sent to the Antarctic for over a year; it was a location with conditions difficult to endure.

Mercer said the end of January ushered in the period called "The Ice." It was the time when the Ross Sea is frozen and ships cannot reach McMurdo. The Ice lasted until the beginning of Oc-tober. During those months, the crew of 25 men was completely isolated. The extended time without sunlight added to the isola-tion. "Psychologically, you need to be able to handle that. You're going into a situation where you're in perpetual darkness for about three months—there is no light and you're isolated from the outside world," Mercer says.

He compares the psychological tests to today's Minnesota Multiphasic Personality Inventory (MMPI), which is a standard test most companies use to screen applicants to work in the nuclear industry. The tests help determine how well workers feel they can handle certain situations, how sound their rela-tionships are with others—family, friends, crew mates, how they handle being alone, how well they would handle, as Mer-cer puts it, "not being able to get up and go to the corner 7-Eleven to get a Slurpee."

In other words, could applicants be productive and successful when they were relegated to a small geographical location with minimum amenities? Mercer believes these tests were invaluable and taught crew members a lot about themselves.

TRAINING BEGINS

The Army, part of the tri-service operation, handled the entire year of training, held at the SM1 nuclear plant in Fort Belvoir, Virginia.

"It was a tough year for me, academically," Mercer admits. But he had knowledgeable teachers, the majority of whom were senior enlisted instructors with more than ten years in the industry. He and his classmates learned a great deal in a short time. Mercer remembers that these instructors were also good coaches, combining constant encouragement with the program's formal training.

Mercer and his classmates were trained as plant operators, but there were four disciplines included beyond that – mechanical, electrical discipline, instrumentations control, and health physics (now known as RP, or radiation protection).

Mercer started training in September 1969 and finished a year later. Initially, his training centered on Fort Belvoir's SM1 plant. But he soon began working with single-loop pressurized water reactors. All single-loop pressurized water reactors behaved similarly, and though each was designed a little differently—some a bit larger, others a bit smaller each with its own unique "character"— the basic design was the same, and an operator trained on one of them would immediately understand how to operate the others.

After preliminary training, Mercer ended up in the health physics discipline because it was the focus that fit most closely with his background. In the mechanical disciplines, one found welders or people who excelled with pumps, motors or boilers.

The electrical discipline was made up of those with experience as construction electricians. And the instrument control discipline included people who embraced working with wiring and control circuitry.

Mercer says, "I'm a corpsman, so health physics made sense because it had something to do with the body and health. But in reality, I had no choice. To work in any one of the four disciplines, you already had to have an existing level of training in that discipline. We all knew where we were going."

Health physics is an extension of radiation safety programs developed during WWII, growing from the realization that exposure to radioactive materials must be carefully monitored. "Anything before the Manhattan Project was really hit or miss," Mercer says. "The Manhattan Project changed everything."

The course work was challenging. Students had to maintain consistently high scores on all tests. If instructors saw a student falling into the low 80s out of 100, they coached and mentored the student, revisiting specific areas where the trainee showed weakness. The instructor's job was to provide levels of instruction and training that would make the trainees confident power plant operators, and confident radiation-protection personnel.

"They saw that we, like they, had invested a lot of time and commitment to be able to do this. If I flunked out," Mercer says, "I still had a six-year commitment. We had put a lot on the line for this, and they recognized that because they had been there as well."

Not everyone who started the training completed it. In Mercer's class, he remembers, twenty-two started but only sixteen remained at the end of the year. Some were just not cut out for the job; others simply couldn't meet the academic standards.

When Mercer completed training, he worked in the RP area at the SM1 plant at Fort Belvoir. He also worked as the environmental monitor for the plant, taking air, sediment, and fish samples from Fort Belvoir and the Chesapeake Bay area. He analyzed those samples, and turned the results over to the plant's environmental engineers. During that time, he had also begun what was known as "replacement crew training" at Fort Belvoir. They formed a crew of twenty-five personnel with an officer in charge, a senior enlisted man, and then twenty-three military personnel who had gone through the program. That replacement crew training took Mercer an additional year.

OFF TO THE ANTARCTIC

At the end of his replacement crew training, Mercer finally got his chance to go to Antarctica. He spent thirteen months there as one of the crew members on the McMurdo PM3A nuclear plant. This was 1972. Mercer was twenty-eight years old.

To get to the Antarctic, he flew from the United States to Christchurch. He remembers there was a small detachment in Christchurch who was able to get people and material on and off the ice, acting as kind of a port facility. Early in the year, they would fly cavernous Lockheed C-141s, which landed on the ice runway.

Later, around Thanksgiving, the ice runway would become unsafe and could no longer handle aircraft. "You were faced with the Ross Ice Shelf, which is a tremendous glacier that goes hundreds of miles back into the Antarctic continent itself, and then ends right there at McMurdo Station."

At that time, Mercer estimates the glacier was about 100 feet or more above the water at McMurdo. "You could literally see it when you walked out the door." Williams Field, on the glacier, provided the snow runway used to support the rest of the aircraft flying in from New Zealand to Williams Field. There was also a support facility which helped get everything out to the different

Antarctic research experiments on the Antarctic Continent.

Once he arrived at the station, Mercer and his colleagues required even more training. "Our initial training was just to make us nuclear plant operators. But now, as a crew on a different plant, we had to train for that one specifically," Mercer recalls. Some of the older men on the crew had been there before. Because this was their second time on the ice, they were a big help to the newcomers.

Mercer worked with the operations group. He also worked with the senior radiation-protection enlisted man who had been on the ice before. The team was not only getting new plant training, they were getting it from individuals who were familiar with the plant and its operating environment.

There were differences between the SM1 at Fort Belvoir and the PM3A in McMurdo, so they trained in those differences. One key difference was how the steam cycle worked. A part of a steam cycle takes the unused steam through a turbine and then condenses it back into water so it can make steam again. The PM3A, like all power plants in the States, needs a source to cool the steam back into water. At Fort Belvoir, they used water from Chesapeake Bay. But at McMurdo, they used air blasters and pulled cold air out of the environment to condense the steam. "We've got 60 degree water at the Chesapeake Bay, but, for the PM3A, I was dealing with 15 or 20 degrees below temperatures," Mercer explains. "There's lot of things an operator had to do differently. They had to get the levers closed and take the blowers off; otherwise, you're going to wind up with a block of ice."

Mercer and his colleagues were sent in to replace the visiting crew who had been in place. And he noted they were all welcome.

"We each told the man we were sent to relieve, 'I am your replacement. You are going to train me to be able to do my job to meet the standardized requirements.' And the guy there would reply, 'You and I are going to be best of buddies. I'm going to get you the best food I can. And I'm going to make sure that if you have any question, I'm going to do my best to answer it so I can get off the ice.'"

All members of the replacement crew had to go through an oral board exam to ensure their training qualified them to take over. When each new man was qualified in core operations, the person he was replacing could go home. Once the crew member being replaced had departed the ice, Mercer and his teammates would be trained in the operations of their individual disciplines. "It took about a month for me to qualify because it was all brand-new to me." Other individuals had been there before, so their training time was shorter.

Once the new crew came fully on board, there was a time crunch. Maintenance became an issue. Work needed to be completed while the ice was open; they had to make sure they got scheduled maintenance done early in the summer. Because of the impending ice, Mercer noted, "If we needed parts or anything else for necessary maintenance work, then the work had to be done during that brief window of time." Maintenance would take up the majority of the summer. Then the plant would be brought back online with the hope that no more maintenance would be needed until the next summer.

Once maintenance was complete, the crew began cross-training. Because of the isolation, replacement personnel could not be brought in; if someone were sick or injured, the crew needed to be able to carry on. "Not all personnel on the crew would necessarily be cross-trained," Mercer clarifies, "but we had a cadre of extra-trained operators who could give the operating shifts a day off when needed. If somebody got sick, somebody else could walk in and take his place."

The "winter-over" crew was segregated from the staff at Mc-Murdo Station.

"The winter-over team had two functions," he explains. "One was maintaining the station, and the other was to prearranging support for the scientists who came in the summer to do their experiments, making sure their vehicles and anything else they needed had have been repaired, maintained, tested, and was ready to go."

The summer scientists worked primarily at the Cosmic Ray Station, which was about a mile-and-a-half from McMurdo. They manned huge detectors designed to measure cosmic radiation. "But there was one guy who was at the Cosmic Ray Station year round, all by himself. I have no idea how he did it," Mercer marvels. "Nobody was up there with him, but he could come down whenever he wanted."

Part of Mercer's job as an RP was providing environmental monitoring at the Cosmic Ray Station. So he would see the year-round Cosmic Ray scientist every couple of days. "I'd knock on the door, and ask, 'Do you need anything?' He always said yes! He kept the volume of the cosmic radiation detectors turned way up and I could always hear the clickity, clickity, clickity of the detectors."

But sometimes things didn't work as expected. Mercer recounts that, in December of 1972, they faced a challenge they couldn't overcome. The crew had just finished its replacement crew training and was getting ready to do maintenance work. Then the Navy Engineering Command reported there were allegations the station may have some issues with chloride stress corrosion—possibly degradation in the stainless steel.

High levels of chlorides in the presence of oxygen, combined with high temperature and high pressure, can cause stress corrosion and cracking in stainless steel. The crew had to take samples of the insulation that covered a rack of coolant piping, which had stainless steel cladding on the outside and insulation inside. To obtain the sample of the suspect insulation, the stainless steel on the insulation had to be cut away. This work was performed in a high-radiation area and radiation exposure was closely controlled.

Mercer notes the samples showed trace amounts of chlorides, but this was not necessarily the critical issue; it didn't indicate whether there was chloride stress corrosion or not. The Navy ultimately decided to put the plant in a cold shutdown mode and have it reevaluated over the upcoming winter. "What they were saying was we cannot prove beyond a shadow of a doubt that there is no chloride stress corrosion."

Ultimately, testing indicated that any corrosion was well within an acceptable presence of chloride. "But, politically, it became an issue with the pristine nature of the Antarctic continent. What if we ended up with a man-made contamination event on the Antarctic?"

That was something the Navy didn't want to take a chance on. The crew was reduced from twenty-five members to twelve, and this remaining dozen would handle any maintenance still to be done. Mercer was part of the crew that remained at McMurdo.

When the reactor was operating, McMurdo used reactor steam to run flash evaporators, which were used for the desalinization that provided fresh water to the station. When the reactor wasn't operating, backup boilers provided the steam for the flash evaporators. These backup boilers needed maintenance to ensure they would function properly during the forced shutdown.

"From a personal point of view," Mercer recalls, "I think that, in all probability, had they not decided to do the shutdown, there would have been an outcry. We were in the middle of a time period when anti-nuke groups were extremely vocal. And the Navy probably didn't want to take the heat on any problems in Antarctica. It wasn't that they could prove there was a problem, but they couldn't prove there wasn't one."

The crew defueled the reactor, put the existing reactor core in a fuel shipment container, and shipped it back to the United States. The largest source of radioactivity was gone, leaving only the small quantities of residual radioactivity associated with reactor vessels – the piping and some of the steam generators.

When his time at McMurdo came to an end, Mercer was reassigned and transferred to the Naval Submarine Medical Center in New London, where he taught radiation protection for a year and a half. But he never forgot the experience of being at McMurdo.

"I saw the Aurora Australis. Being there around Christmas time was kind of neat because the sun never went down. It would go high into the sky, and, then, at the end of the day, the bottom of the sun would just touch the horizon before it started back up. It's daylight twenty-four hours a day. Then, during the winter solstice, it's totally dark." The highest summer temperature Mercer remembers was 17 degrees. During the winter he faced temperatures of 20 to 40 degrees below zero, with winds and storms roaring off of the continent.

But, amazingly, everyone remained healthy. "Nobody died. We had no medical emergencies. We had a good medical staff, and there were no medical complications at all."

There is no longer a nuclear power plant at McMurdo. Ultimately, the decision was made to not only pull out the reactor core after the concern about chloride stress corrosion but also to completely dismantle the station. They wanted to remove every trace of the nuclear site and leave the continent as environmentally pristine as they had found it.

A BRIGHT FUTURE FOR THE VALUE OF
RADIATION PROTECTION

When Mercer considers what he would most like to pass on to newcomers in the nuclear industry about McMurdo, he says, "I think I would tell them that I was always supplied with state-of-the art equipment during the time."

For example, early on, he utilized something called a multi-channel analyzer, which detected gamma rays, and he relied upon that information to determine the type of radioactive material present. At that time, it was the very best equipment available. He also had a 100-channel analyzer made up strictly of electronic tubes. It had numerous switches and potentiometers, and he could analyze a sample using a basic calculator and a slide rule. It took a couple of hours to collect a sample and calculate the activity in a sample by individual radionuclides and quantity. (Today, a technician can do it in the amount of time it takes to collect the sample, about ten minutes, and the computation of the radioactivity takes about five seconds!)

Mercer says, "I'd like people to recognize how much the RP arena has grown to provide better results in a shorter amount of time and with far greater accuracy. The equipment the students have now makes their jobs a lot easier. And they can be more confident about the accuracy of the results they're getting." He admits that, in the early days, results were subject to human error because of the limitations of the tools being used. "There were a lot of times when I would second-guess myself as to whether the results were right or not. Was I off a decimal point? I would go back and do the work twice, just to make sure."

Today's nuclear technicians have computers that can take samples. And the resulting reports provide details displaying all the information they need, including any warning levels requiring attention.

Mercer realizes the importance of this. "With these new analysis systems, we can establish valuable and realistic warning levels. This is so important because it can have a real effect on people and on the way you provide protection. This will give the new generation of RP techs more confidence and provide even better protection of people from harmful radiation." And this, of course, is the goal of nuclear technicians everywhere.

LESSONS LEARNED

- Besides aptitude and academic prowess, psychological makeup is also taken into account since not all nuclear workers are suited to every job in the industry.

- The nuclear industry is constantly using new state-of-the-art tools to help improve accuracy and efficiency.

- Training in the industry is not easy and will challenge you.

CHAPTER 5

◆

LEON WALTERS, PhD

VP of Fuel Design at Advanced Reactor Concepts, L.L.C. (ARC)

*It takes a huge team effort to get all the pieces together. Some are
young and bright people; some are older experienced people
who can pass down their knowledge. It's a huge puzzle to
manage something like this, and I would say the toughest part is
getting the right kind of people with the right initiative to fit in
with the personality of the group, where everyone is working in
harmony on a common goal.*

RAISED IN THE SMALL MONTANA TOWN OF ANACONDA, WHERE THE
copper smelter was the primary source of employment, Leon
Walters lived in a modest house on the poor side of town. Captain
of the football team and president of his class, Walters excelled
in high school. But when he graduated, he really didn't know
what he wanted to do with the rest of his life. Actually, he says,

"I wanted to stay in Montana and be a forest ranger, but my dad wouldn't hear of it."

His father knew his son well and was concerned that he would fritter away his time hunting and fishing, losing track of a career path.

FINDING A CAREER PATH IN ATOMIC ENERGY

Walters's older brother was at Purdue University, studying to be an aeronautical engineer. So Purdue seemed as good a college destination as any. Still, Walters didn't know what career path he would take. All he was sure of was that, although he'd be going to school in Indiana, he wanted to return to the West after college. "I thought," he recalls, "maybe if I major in metallurgical engineering, I can get back to the mountains. My thought process – metals come from rocks, rocks come from mountains; it was as simple as that."

Walters enrolled in 1957. His family expected Walters to have trouble succeeding at a school as large and sophisticated as Purdue, but he did superbly well, graduating in 1961 at the top of his class with a bachelor's degree in metallurgical engineering. Urged by his professors to continue on to a master's degree, Walters applied for, and was awarded, an Atomic Energy Commission fellowship.

The AEC fellowship funded three years of studies, including tuition and a living allowance. Walters enjoyed his studies, earning his doctorate degree in 1965. He was twenty-five years old, a PhD, now married and raising a family. "And then my problem was – how and where did I want to start my career?" Although his Purdue professors wanted him to stay and teach, Walters remained true to his original goal of returning to the West.

He applied for jobs throughout the West, in Denver, Washington, and California, as well as at Los Alamos and Sandia

National Labs, both in New Mexico. He received identical offers from Los Alamos and Sandia. He says, "That was as far West as I could get. But New Mexico is a beautiful place and I accepted the job at Sandia, a nuclear weapons laboratory." Walters spent a rewarding five years at Sandia.

It was the end of the 1960s, and the climate for the nuclear industry was changing. SALT I, the first series of Strategic Arms Limitation Talks, began in November 1969 and extended to May 1972. During that period, the United States and the Soviet Union negotiated the first agreements to place limits and restraints on nuclear stockpiles. Walters saw this as a sign the funding for nuclear weapons development was going to dry up.

Serendipitously, about the same time, one of Walters's former professors at Purdue was asked if he could recommend someone to work at Idaho's fast breeder reactors—nuclear reactors that create more fissile material than they consume. His professor approached Walters. "I wasn't that interested," he confesses, "but I thought I'd go to Idaho for an interview because it was close to home, and I could visit my parents in Montana." To Walters' surprise, he found the job offer appealing and accepted the position with the Idaho facility of the Argonne National Laboratory. He found working on fast breeder reactors fascinating and they would become the focus of his career.

The concept of breeder reactors goes back to 1947, when Enrico Fermi (often called the father of nuclear power) met with other experts after the termination of the Manhattan Project with the goal of developing nuclear power programs for civilian electricity. It was during those meetings they developed the concept of breeding. Walters explains that normal nuclear reactors, called "light water reactors," use little of the mined natural uranium — the fuel used is made up of four to five percent of enriched uranium. When you mine uranium, only about seven-tenths are fissionable (U235). The rest (U238) is useless in regular reactors. But if you start a reactor with fissionable U235, and then surround the reactor with U238 that's not fissionable, it can be "bred" to capture neutrons with plutonium 239, which, in turn, can be used in fission. Thus, in a breeder reactor, you can use all the mined uranium and instead of having 200 or 300 years' worth of fuel inventory for a normal reactor, you have fuel for several thousand years from the same source uranium.

In 1951, in the Idaho desert, nuclear scientists developed a reactor they called External Breeder 1 (EBR1), which would demonstrate to the world the breeder concept. This was the first reactor to generate useful electricity from nuclear power. They went on to build a pilot-sized demonstration plant called EBR2. Walters was just twenty-nine years old when he moved to Idaho, beginning as an EBR2 staff member, learning all he could about radiation technology, but Walters's primary assignment was to develop ways to fabricate the fuel and demonstrate reactor performance.

While doing that research, he also successfully managed and improved three fabrication facilities. He proudly notes that, over the years, he managed the 200 to 300 engineers who developed the fuel process still used today. That phase of his career ended just before the year 2000. His next step was to become the Director of Engineering for Argonne National Laboratory.

NUCLEAR POWER TO CREATE TRANSPORTATION FUEL

Walters then turned his attention to a new idea, "What the world really needed was a transportation fuel that could be developed with nuclear power. So I took on the job of trying to convince the world nuclear electricity could generate hydrogen, hydrogen could be used in fuel cells, and fuel cells could be used as transportation fuel." During that period of his career, he and his team racked up major accomplishments that significantly moved forward the idea of a transition to a hydrogen economy.

That mission took him to Canada, where he worked to develop the concept with several noted colleagues, including Jeff Ballard (often called the father of hydrogen fuel cells), Sandy Stewart, "the father of electrolysis," and David Scott, head of engineering at the University of Victoria.

Walters says, "We had people who generated hydrogen, people who worked the fuel cells, and then nuclear power from Dave Wade and me at Argonne National Laboratory. So we had all three pieces necessary to succeed." This team put together the concept of developing hydrogen fuel cell cars from nuclear power.

Walters believes hydrogen will eventually become transportation fuel for the world, because, as he explains, "if you look at the way energy is used worldwide, it kind of carves itself up in thirds. About a third of it is used for electrical energy, which is made primarily from coal, along with nuclear power, hydropower, and some wind power. About a third of the energy used in the world is for high-temperature processing of steel and chemicals. The last, and very important, is fuel for transportation."

Generally, all transportation energy comes from fossil fuel. Walters points out that there are two options for reducing this reliance on fossil fuel: 1) a battery-powered car which generates electricity to charge the batteries as a transportation fuel, or 2) a nuclear generator electricity to produce hydrogen and fuel cells. Walters and his colleagues have worked hard to make the latter a reality.

However, he became concerned the knowledge they had worked so hard to develop and accumulate over the last fifty years wasn't being properly maintained. To ensure that didn't happen, Walters and others from around the globe created an initiative to preserve the relevant data. "We realized that a lot of us were getting old," he acknowledges. "And we needed to keep that technology alive."

FACING CHALLENGES

"We had so many challenges!" Walters says.

The biggest challenge he faced centered on integral fast reactor projects. He and his team were reprocessing fuel-technology that fell out of favor during Jimmy Carter's presidency. According to Walters, President Carter was dead set against reprocessing fuel because of his concern regarding nuclear proliferation (in reprocessing fuel for breeder reactors, you can end up with plutonium and potentially build a bomb). So, "by killing reprocessing," Walters notes, "Carter essentially killed the breeder project."

Those were dark days for Argonne; it looked as if they would lose their entire fast breeder project. The big challenge was to somehow develop a processing system that would be proliferation-proof, thus nullifying Carter's concerns.

To accomplish this, Walters and his team needed the fuel to reach a "burnup," or utilization factor, where at least ten percent of the fuel could be fissioned before being reprocessed. At that time, though, they had fuel burnup at just under two percent. It was a daunting challenge to increase the burnup factor by some five-fold, but "we developed a concept," Walters says.

Walters and his colleagues at Argonne discovered a paper by British scientist D.C. Barnes, which offered ideas for making fuel burn off at a higher percentage. Barnes argued that if you let fuel expand enough during irradiation, the gas bubbles would interconnect and release the gas from the fuel. He compared it to lava flowing from a volcano – very porous, and when it cools down the gas tries to get out. The primary technical stumbling block was trying to institute the concept of a low-density fuel that could reheat and not fracture the cladding of the nuclear fuel and still get a high utilization factor of ten percent.

The concept stated if the fuel wasn't tightly fit in the cladding, and enough space remained for it to expand, then those gas bubbles would interconnect and release the gas. And, if the volume of cladding were large enough to receive that gas without stressing the cladding, the driving force pushing on the cladding that caused it to fracture would be removed. "It was a simple, simple idea," Walters says. They made certain that seventy-five percent of the volume was fuel and twenty-five percent of the volume between the fuel and the cladding was empty, thus allowing the fuel to expand and the gas bubbles to interconnect, which would release gas of a properly-sized volume.

During U235 fission, a neutron will strike U235 and split it. The result is two atoms of fission products, plus at least two more neutrons, and those two neutrons make four neutrons, causing a chain reaction. The neutrons fly around in the reactor, find the U238, and convert it to plutonium. The neutrons also do damage to the cladding. The neutrons come out of the fuel, go right through the cladding, and find U238.

Walters explains the process. "A lot happens to the cladding when the neutrons strike. It can swell, become brittle, and fail. So you have to find cladding that won't swell, that won't become brittle too soon. Different groups around the world worked hard on different alloy compositions, starting with 304L stainless steel. They then went to 316, which swelled less. They put some titanium in the 316-coated steel, and that swelled less. We were moving along the line, doing better and better."

He then attributes a breakthrough to French researchers who went to a different crystal structure entirely, a ferritic material called HT9 that didn't seem to swell at all. He points out that millions of dollars were spent on developing the effective cladding.

Walters and his team started the project in late 1980 and created the first experimental fuel in the reactor in January 1981. "Once we demonstrated ten percent," he says, "this whole new initiative caught on, and we were able to keep it going until 1994 when the reactor was shut down." Although at the time it appeared this might mean the end of this type of fuel and of breeding reactors, there are now several concepts based upon the principles proposed and demonstrated by Walters's team.

Walters says, "All our work has been carried forward, and my expectation is that, within the next decade, we'll see one of these reactors emerge—the breeding will be back."

Walters asks rhetorically, "If you only get ten percent utilization, what happens to the fuel you don't use? In the breeder cycle, you have plutonium that you breed in, and you end up with U235 that you haven't used, so you can process that chemically and put it back in the next reactor for the fuel there."

A COOPERATIVE/COMPETITIVE ENVIRONMENT

The nuclear industry began before the Second World War, focusing primarily on weaponry. Across the world, scientists were trying to harness nuclear power. Everything was done in secret, with little sharing of information. An exception was the U.S. and England, where there were joint efforts.

After the war, however, President Eisenhower was instrumental in opening up communications and collaboration in the nuclear industry. He wanted civilian nuclear energy to be shared by the world, and Eisenhower continued to push for this collaboration even after his presidency ended. Walters remembers that the level of international cooperation during the 1970s and part of the 1980s was tremendous.

When Walters was working on EBR2, scientists from all over the world were invited to Idaho, where they could run both fuel and cladding experiments. Walters says, "Our little home in Idaho Falls became an international conclave. We had Russians, the French, and a lot of interaction with the British, Japanese, and Koreans.' He adds that information was freely shared with all, including the Russians.

Within that cooperative environment, there was some competitiveness. Walters explains that different countries had different approaches to building a breeder reactor. The two primary methods were the pool-type reactor and the loop-type reactor.

Initially, both the U.S. and France chose to build the pool type. But later, the U.S. changed its approach, moving to a loop type. The Japanese were also building a loop reactor, yet their design was different, leading to friendly competition—each country wanted to prove their design was safer and more effective.

There was also competition over fuel types – ceramic fuel versus metal fuel. Ceramic was preferred initially, but metal fuel won in the end. According to Walters, this major competition lasted for fifty years. Also, countries became competitive about their approaches to cladding. But Walters stresses these were healthy competitions, and different combinations of approaches were experimented with, resulting in extensive shared data.

But some of that spirit of cooperation ended when the Cold War escalated and the Russians stopped sharing information. Further, according to Walters, the French recognized the commercial implications of non-military nuclear energy and became more competitive than cooperative.

Walters points out that there was also competition among different U.S. companies. Westinghouse in Hanford, General Electric in Santa Monica, Argonne outside Chicago, and Brookhaven in Long Island all had similar groups working on solutions. And not only were they competing technologically to find the best approaches, they were also competing for funding. But Walters insists it was great fun. "It was very enjoyable. Even though I competed hard with people in these different groups, we were still the best of friends."

WORKING WITH GOOD PEOPLE

Besides technical challenges, Walters believes the most vital consideration is hiring the right people. The industry needs intelligent, dedicated young graduates of all levels in physics, chemistry, nuclear engineering, metallurgy, and material science.

He says, "It takes a huge team effort to get all the pieces together. Some are young, bright people; some are older, experienced people who can pass down their knowledge. It's a huge puzzle to manage something like this, and I would say the toughest part is getting the right kind of people with the right initiative to fit in with the personality of the group, where everyone is working in harmony on a common goal."

Although Walters was primarily focused on the technical aspects, as a manager, he made it a point to spend at least two hours every day visiting his team members to discuss their technical challenges. "I never lost track of the people themselves," he says, unlike some managers who don't take the time to maintain personal contact and, often, are unsuccessful as a result. He advocates for managers to get to know their staff members' families and hobbies in addition to how things are going on the job. He acknowledges, "It's tough to do when you have 200 or 300 people, but I think I knew my people well. It's the people, all the way down. The janitor is just as important as the PhD scientist. He's part of the group, and he is vital to making it all run well."

Walters stresses that you have to keep people informed. If your administrative staff knows what's going on technically, they will not only be happier in their jobs, but also they will be more useful to the team. "That, to me, was the key to being successful over my whole career."

Working with a team can be a challenge. Walters says you must start with an excellent team leader but stresses a successful team is the product of many individual personalities. "You don't want people who are grandstanding, who are trying to take credit where credit isn't due, and you want to have a team leader who can point out the people responsible for the achievement." Everyone has to feel that his or her contribution is significant and acknowledged.

Another key to success with team projects is understanding the mission. "Mission is so important," he states. "When we didn't have a defined mission, we struggled in most of the laboratories. We actually went through three mission changes with the reactor project." Defining the mission means all team members know what they are driving toward, and when they've achieved the right results.

Walters also points out a major part of the life of a manager in the nuclear industry is securing funding, which requires making presentations to the Department of Energy as well as other funding sources. He remembers the funding challenges for the integral fast reactor project, when he was working on cladding development. His program wasn't "too big, maybe five or ten million dollars," he says. "It was really working well." And then the Department of Energy decided to move all the research associated with cladding to Hanford and instructed Walters to transfer all his data to that facility. This meant he was losing all his funding. He was given the option of moving there, but he didn't want to move. "That was my biggest disappointment. I did lose that project for a while, but I'm very proud of the work we did."

LOOKING BACK ON HIS CAREER WITH PRIDE

As Walters looks back on his career, two accomplishments stand out for him.

The first was his work on the development of hydrogen fuel cells. "I think the greatest moment I had was being able to develop a fuel with a high burn-off. I am gratified to be one of the pioneers in development of the hydrogen fuel cell cars and hydrogen generated nuclear power." He is proud that, after all those years of research, many people are still working on the technology his team created. There are at least four reactors using this technology and the concept is continually moving forward. "Knowing someday, maybe, I'll live to see those concepts commercialized, I feel comfortable with all of that," Walters says.

The second success he is particularly proud of was when he issued a challenge to preserve the nuclear knowledge base. Walters initially wrote several papers on the importance of maintaining this information, presenting those papers around the world. He gathered people from laboratories around the world, as well as from the International Atomic Energy Agency (IAEA).

These nuclear scientists were made aware that a generation of nuclear workers was on the verge of retirement. They appreciated the problem that a loss of that firsthand knowledge would create. Walters went to the Department of Defense, where they had a similar problem and were struggling to preserve their own information. "One of the big things we did that really helped was at the 2000 Reno American Nuclear Society. I was the chairman of that conference, and we created that knowledge preservation at that conference in the form of the nuclear knowledge resolution team."

The ten members of the initial team enthusiastically carried the banner and it went forward from there. Several laboratories then took on the challenge, as did the IAEA. And that work is continuing.

Walters has a number of thoughts he'd like to share with the incoming generation of nuclear workers. "I tell my sons that whatever you're doing today, do it the best you can." He also stresses jobs in the nuclear industry can't be about ego and self-promotion. "Your job is to make your boss look good, and, if you can't do that find another job. If you do good work, you will get the acknowledgement you need without seeking it out."

Money should not be a major concern. Walters assures young people entering the field that money is the last thing they need to worry about. "If you do good work, you will be compensated adequately. Don't get that backward!"

As for what area of the nuclear industry he recommends entering, he says, "If a grandchild of mine asked, I'd tell them to go into metallurgical engineering. Of course, I'm prejudiced, but if you look at any technology, the ultimate limitation is materials. You can only go so far unless you have a type of material that will withstand the extreme temperatures, environment, corrosion, whatever. I can't think of any industry that's not material dependent."

But his most important lesson is the need for absolute integrity in the nuclear industry. Walters insists industry workers be completely honest with how they view experimental results and how they interact with people. "Don't embellish anything from a scientific point of view, and, for God's sake, don't falsify any information. It will hurt you and the industry as a whole."

And a final piece of advice, "There is no such thing as a bad question. Don't ever be embarrassed to ask for clarification!" And this goes for management as well. Walters advises not to lecture, just ask questions of your team and listen to the answers. He believes this leads to a free exchange of ideas and good relationships among a working group.

LESSONS LEARNED

■ Honesty and integrity are paramount. No matter your role, present your results and findings honestly, without embellishment. Never change or falsify information, even if it seems to be advantageous to you or your project.

■ Make sure you understand the mission of the job you and your team are charged with.

■ Know what you are trying to achieve and what is expected of you. And, if you aren't sure, ask questions.

■ You will be appreciated and acknowledged for good work. The nuclear industry is built on team efforts and collaboration.

CHAPTER 6

◆

SAED MIRZADEH, PhD

Medical Radioisotope Program
Nuclear Security and Isotope Technology Division
Oak Ridge National Laboratory (ORNL)

The age of science—when we chemists or physicists or scientists
go to the basement of the chemistry department, are happy with
the results, and just publish our papers—well, that age is over.
Anybody who thinks it's still that way is just naïve.
Nowadays, you have to sell your product.

"I WAS GOING TO BE AN ARCHITECT," SAED MIRZADEH RECALLS.
"At least, that's what I had planned when I started college at the
National University of Iran."

But his oldest brother started college at the same time, also
choosing architecture as a major. Mirzadeh felt having two ar-
chitects in one family would create something of a competition,
so he changed his field of study to chemistry.

Then, after a year, his brother switched to linguistics!

Mirzadeh realized he would lose too many credit hours if he went back to the architecture program after his brother switched majors, so he stuck with chemistry. It turned out he had a knack for chemistry and thermodynamics. "I really liked the physics part of it. I was fascinated with nuclear phenomena and what happens with the nucleus."

Mirzadeh continued on the nuclear path he had begun. He focused on nuclear chemistry and radiochemistry, with additional studies in astrophysics and nuclear physics, ultimately receiving his PhD in physical chemistry (radiochemistry) from the University of New Mexico in 1978.

PUTTING HIS BACKGROUND TO USE IN CURING DISEASE

After a one-year stint as a research associate at the Los Alamos National Laboratory Medical Radioisotope Program, Mirzadeh went on to Brookhaven National Laboratory (BNL) on Long Island in 1980. During his two-year postdoctoral appointment, he primarily focused on a hard-core nuclear chemistry search for short-lived radionuclides. After his postdoc, he worked at BNL, creating an isotope known as astatine-211, an alpha emitter used in cancer therapy.

Mirzadeh explains his role was to make the isotope and then transfer it to a ferry captain on Long Island. The captain voyaged to New London, Connecticut, and handed off the isotope to a messenger, who then delivered the package to Harvard Medical School in Boston. Mirzadeh did this for a year, until he was transferred to another department, where he worked on different isotopes, again for medical applications.

Mirzadeh remained at Brookhaven until 1987. He then moved to the National Institutes of Health (NIH), primarily because people there claimed the isotope he was making didn't work. "What do you mean it doesn't work?" he asked them. "I made it!" So he took a two-year sabbatical at NIH to see firsthand how they were using his isotope. He soon realized the nature of the issue.

The scientists there added his isotopes to antibodies they had designed to fight cancer cells. They engineered the antibodies to travel to a specific site, then they placed radioactive payloads on top of the antibodies and injected this into the bloodstream.

But the chemistry must ensure these metal ions didn't "fall off" during the ride. Mirzadeh says, "There are a huge number of proteins in the human body whose jobs are to go around and pick up the things that aren't normal, such as the metal ions they don't think should be there. This chemistry well, it turned out to be very difficult to do, because there is no protection for the metal ions when in the body."

Mirzadeh says, "You have to make a basket with a lot of arms called "chelae," from the Greek name for claw. These chelae have about eight "arms" that lock onto the metal ions and do not release them under normal conditions; the other end of this basket is attached to the protein or antibody. It's like a payload, very much like a torpedo. The radio-labeled antibody is injected into the body and eventually finds the cancer site, latches onto it, and then, when this radioactivity decays, it irradiates at the cellular level."

This approach addresses problems with current radiation therapy, which, while useful, is applied externally and is non-discriminate, killing healthy tissue as well as targeted cancer tissue.

With the method he was working on, the irradiation path length was limited to 5 to 10 cell diameters (about 50 to100 micrometers), depending on the range of the particle the radioisotope emits. So the radioisotope , which emits the alpha particle, has very limited radiation toxicity, due to the significant reduction of irradiation to other normal tissue or bone marrow.

The patient who receives this alpha pharmaceutical does not suffer from toxicity. This is where Mirzadeh's interest lies. "I got involved primarily with the therapy," he says, "looking at the radioisotopes that emit high-energy alpha particles. That's the main work that I'm doing here, primarily looking at two isotopes."

One of these is actinium-225; this has a ten day half-life and emits a very high- energy alpha particle, which, if you attach it to the antibody, delivers it exactly where you want it to go.

PRODUCING RADIOISOTOPES TO BATTLE CANCER

Mirzadeh came to the Nuclear Medicine Program at Oak Ridge National Laboratory (ORNL) in 1989, after two years with the NIH. He supports a group doing leukemia studies at Memorial Sloan Kettering Cancer Center in New York.

He says, "Currently, they are in phase two of human trials, attaching actinium to their antibodies and delivering it to the leukemic cell. That's actually one of the simplest forms of the drug delivery, because the cancer cell is accessible in the bloodstream. You needn't wait for the diffusion through tissues or any other matter. So, with one pass, within two or three minutes, we can lodge in all these antibodies that are designed to irradiate the leukemic cell. It has been reported that, in some patients, this approach killed about two kilograms of a tumor. This is very exciting for me because I can see the application of my efforts, and it is working!"

There is a problem, however. He explains, "I cannot support the full extent of this research due to the limited availability of actinium-225, which was extracted some time ago from an isotope of thorium called thorium-229. Thorium-229 was extracted from the uranium isotope U-233, which is a highly fissile material.

"In other words," Mirzadeh says, "when you add a neutron to the nucleus of U-235, it splits. It gives you two neutrons back.

So if you have two other U-235 atoms present, the two neutrons from the first split will hit two atoms of U-235, and then each gives you two neutrons. Before you know it, you have a chain reaction. Each split of U-235 releases enormous energy—per unit mass some 1,000-fold more than energy from chemical reactions, such as burning fossil fuel. This is the principle of the fission process that governs the operation of nuclear power plants, where the number of neutrons is managed and generated heat is removed and used to generate electricity."

He continues, "U-233 was even more fissile than U-235. After WWII, they were worried there were not enough uranium mines in the U.S. So they made U-233. Turned out there was plenty of uranium in the U.S., therefore there was no need for U-233.

"The actinium we are providing to the Sloan Kettering Cancer Center comes from the waste material generated when purifying the original U-233. They stored all the waste associated with the production of U-233, including the Th-229, in stainless steel waste tanks. We purified this waste material and made it useful. Unfortunately, we can no longer use U-233 due to security issues, which is why I am focusing on an alternative way of making these isotopes."

When Mirzadeh first came to ORNL, John Maddox, a DOE program manager, told him there was U-233 at ORNL. "Why don't you just go there and see if you can extract the actinium?" Maddox asked.

Maddox and Mirzadeh were naïve enough to believe they could just get the U-233, extract Th-229, purify it, and use it as a mother stock for production of Ac-225. But after two years Mirzadeh abandoned the effort.

By coincidence, somebody told him about a foreign company that was buying waste sludge from the bottom of one of those old tanks. When he asked why they were buying the sludge,

Mirzadeh was only told the company was paying quite a lot of money for each kilogram of the material. He immediately understood why.

"I wondered how the company buying the sludge knew it wasn't just some old material—in other words, they must have known what it was. So I contacted the person involved and insisted they stop selling this stuff. He told me they had a contract to sell the company two kilograms; they had already sent one kilogram to them and were waiting to send the second." Mirzadeh insisted they not send it until he could investigate further.

This company had contracted for a specific amount of a material (the aforementioned thorium-229) to be extracted from these two kilograms. Mirzadeh points out the company had made a mistake! They were actually able to extract the full amount from the one kilogram already sent, fulfilling the contract. The ORNL contract office was then able to contact the buyer and tell them the contract was satisfied, because they had all the extracted material they had required; therefore, the second kilogram was not going to be sent. The company sued but later withdrew their lawsuit.

Mirzadeh was then able to get access to the rest of the sludge in the tank and found there was additional material the buyer didn't even think about.

He explains the process. "Raschig rings, which are pieces of tube, approximately equal in length and diameter, are used in large numbers as a packed bed within columns for distillations and other chemical engineering processes. The Raschig rings they used for the extraction were made of Pyrex (the brand name for Borosilicate glass, which is made with silica and boron trioxide), basically the same basic material used in chemistry labs. But what the boron does is pick up neutrons—boron reacts with the neutrons.

"They put these Raschig rings in the tanks, and a neutron flux never reaches the point of a runaway fission process, and boron keeps the neutron in check. Over thirty years' time, the majority of the thorium isotope I was interested in — the parent of my actinium — moved into this glass. Our team picked up the whole garbage can full of these Raschig rings, put acid over it, shook it, and ended up getting all the thorium out of them."

Most of his current material has actually come from the thorium recovered from the Raschig rings. In addition, the company that had originally bought the sludge sold the material to Germany, and it's now stored in Karshu at the Institute of Trans Uranium Isotopes. The Russians also have some U-233 production. Mirzadeh say, "So, among the three of us, we are providing all the Ac-225 being used. But it still isn't enough."

WORKER, NOT MANAGER

Throughout his career in nuclear medicine research, Mirzadeh has always focused on the research, never looking to move into management.

"I don't want to be a manager; I never was a manager. I don't sign the paychecks of the people who work with me. Technically, I work with them, they report to me. But for administration, I have a group leader, a manager; that's his job."

Another reason he doesn't believe he would be a good manager is he doesn't have a political mind. If asked a question, he will answer without hesitation, without considering the political ramifications. He points out this isn't wise if one is managing a program. One wrong answer may jeopardize the whole program.

Yet he doesn't dismiss the importance of management. "There is no doubt that these days you need excellent management," he is quick to say. He realizes you need people who are adept at politics. But, he adds, "You have to accept that the age of science—

when we scientists were happy with results and just published our papers—well, that age is over. Anybody who thinks it's still that way is just naïve. Nowadays, you have to sell your product."

Mirzadeh points out you must convince the public that what you're doing is worth the investment. After all, he has never had fixed funding; his research has been supported from public sources and grants. Throughout his career, he's always had to compete for national funds from numerous grant institutions, and he still writes proposals and brings in money to fund his group's work.

THE CHALLENGE OF FUNDING RESEARCH TO FIND CURES

Although competing for grants isn't how he likes to spend his time, he recognizes it is vital to continuing good research. He warns that, if you choose a career in scientific research, you must become adept at finding financial support for your work. Although he says luck can be a part of it, he believes "a good portion of successfully finding funds is persistence and a clear vision."

He advises young folks considering nuclear medicine or science today to understand the necessity of grant and proposal writing. He says you have to develop and sell your ideas to the people approving the grants. You need to convince them these ideas deserve a chance.

"I mean, ideas in your lab book don't get you a grant; they don't take you anywhere near the point that your project is sellable." And you have to have an open mind to new perspectives. Mirzadeh warns you can't just work in isolation, "You have to interact with the people on the grant committees, you have to listen to them, and you have to take the criticism."

Securing grants can be very frustrating. "I have failed many times on proposals, like anybody else," he admits. But he says you can't be derailed by a negative response. "You learn; you cannot just bang your head against the wall. It's not going to solve the problem. If you fail, you just have to pick yourself up and come at it from a different angle."

MAKING A CONTRIBUTION

Mirzadeh is proud of his colleagues and what they have accomplished as a "good, tight team." They have been successful at creating and shipping actinium that has helped many patients. But past success does not mean they can be any less meticulous in their current work. "We cannot make errors; somebody could get hurt because we made an error in our preparation," he says. "And we have to be fast-paced and timely because there are a very limited number of patients who are on this schedule. We have to deliver. There is no alternative."

When told he has contributed significantly to the treatment of cancer, Mirzadeh modestly states, "I don't want to say 'significantly.' But I am comfortable with my contribution to science." He insists the most important thing to him is being of service and knowing he's doing some good for humanity, that he's improving the quality of life for some people and giving them a chance at a future they might not have had. "That's what drives me."

And that motivation is something no one can take away, even when he has to jump through hoops to get funding and approval. He is more than willing to be a salesman for the research he believes in. "When you make a decision to go do something, you just have to sacrifice whatever you must to accomplish it. I was always like that. When I make a commitment, I do not get discouraged. I do not back off."

When reminded that what he is doing is saving people's lives, Mirzadeh is again modest, but admits, "It's a good feeling." He points out his team is also dedicated to the same concept, citing one of the team members who had lost her sister to cancer. "She just wants to get even," he says.

Even though he and his team might not receive accolades from patients and their families—the physicians are the ones they thank—Mirzadeh insists that's fine with him. "We get feedback and we know when our work is in demand."

They've also been sending their actinium to Karshu, Germany. The German group is doing some clinical trials in Poland on brain tumors, and the results have been impressive.

Mirzadeh says, "Again, it's the same concept. After removing the primary tumor in the brain, they attach the isotopes to the antibody. Then they inject—or place into the cavity of the brain—an antibody that has the actinium on it. The actinium destroys the balance of the tumor that could not be removed surgically. They're sometimes disappointed I can't support them as much as they would like, but the program in the U.S. is moving on to the next phase—which is an alternative method of developing the isotopes."

Although curing cancer is the main focus of his research, he and his team are also working on a side project, this one involving another alpha emitter. This emitter is not designed to cure cancer, but rather to eliminate bone cancer-related pain for terminal patients who typically must rely upon barbiturates. "There is nothing you can do to cure the disease, but you can relieve the pain," he says. This isotope not only works well, but it also has no side effects. Mirzadeh and his team are currently gearing up for mass production on that isotope, as well as the one for curing cancer.

Mirzadeh may still have occasional dreams of being an architect but says, "I have no regrets." Nor should he. How many people can actually say they are helping to win the fight against cancer?

LESSONS LEARNED

- Attention to detail is paramount. You will encounter obstacles in your job, but you have to make sure you complete the job accurately before moving on.

- Persistence is crucial, no matter what one choses to do in life. If you want or believe in something, stay focused and try a different avenue if you hit a roadblock.

- You don't often get thanks for the results of the final application of your work. You have to find personal satisfaction in your work, while understanding the larger impact.

CHAPTER 7

◆

MICHAEL TURNBOW

General Manager, Inspection and Testing Services
Tennessee Valley Authority (TVA)

*I never did a single day of industrial engineering; but all my
training in industrial engineering—the math, the science, and
even the coursework—have applied in one way or another to
everything I do every day.*

"If you're one of those lucky ones, I guess it's ten percent that actually, absolutely know what they're going to do when they grow up, God bless you. If you're the other ninety percent, listen to me, I have a story for you," Michael Turnbow says about his start in the nuclear industry.

"When I finished college, I was going to be an industrial engineer, so I was looking for a job that would be associated with something like that. The nuclear industry was taking off about that time, and a company called Chicago Bridge and Iron was building reactors and other components for different power plants across the country. I went to work for the company in Birmingham, Alabama, where they had an engineering training program. I had no idea what I wanted to do inside that company. All I knew was I had a job."

He continued, "I liked what I had seen in the company, and nuclear power sounded exciting. It was complicated – like a Swiss watch with lots of large pieces — huge, redundant systems, big pressure vessels. Pipes going everywhere! It was a massive undertaking to build one of these things. I started my career in nuclear and began to really get into it. They put me through a training program where you spent six months in each department, including the QA department with nondestructive testing (NDT) and quality control (QC).

"The people there must have told the person who ended up being my boss that I seemed interested in NDT, because, when I finished my internship inside the company, I was approached and asked if I wanted to get involved. I went for it because it seemed exciting, and here I am, thirty-something years later. It's all I've ever done, I never did a single day of industrial engineering; but all my training in industrial engineering, the math, the science, and even the coursework, has applied one way or another to everything I do every day."

Trying to do things faster, better, cheaper—that's what industrial engineering is all about; and that training didn't go to waste in Turnbow's career.

BEGINNING A CAREER IN THE NUCLEAR INDUSTRY

"I found myself, over the years, wanting to always do better. Let me leave you all that message – never stop looking up. You don't want just a job just to say, 'Boy, I've got me a job, and here I am.'

Once you've got the job, you should immediately start pursuing the next better position, whether it's in that company or outside of it."

So Turnbow followed that path and moved from job to better job, company to company. "I left Chicago Bridge and went to work with Teledyne Brown Engineering in Decatur, Alabama. I went from what we call in our industry a certified Level II, where you do the inspections and record them, to a Level III certification, where you perform final evaluations and solve problems. I had the highest level of certification you could get because I had attained so much experience and was able to pass the certification test. So, the money gets a little better, the pressure gets much higher, the responsibilities broaden, the problems happen everywhere, and they come and get you to solve them."

After a time at Teledyne, Turnbow put in an application at the Tennessee Valley Authority (TVA). "I knew that was going to be a big deal when I started working at the world's largest four-unit nuclear plant, located in Hartsville, Tennessee. I went from doing the work and being the tech leader, to helping set up a school to train and certify sufficient personnel to staff TVA's construction sites, because TVA was building seventeen nuclear plants! Each of those seventeen units would have about eighty people. In a three-year period, I taught 500 people – as fast as we could bring them in. We were trying to fill the vacant positions with qualified, certified people."

Turnbow offers another piece of advice for those pursuing a nuclear career. "Another little trick here is you may think you know something, but you don't really know it until you teach it. Once you teach it for a little while, then you can really say you know the subject. I call those times gifts from God. Sometimes things happen and you are put in situations that change your life beyond anything you can imagine. All along the way, I didn't want to do some of those things I ended up having to do, but in the end, almost every time it was a valuable lesson and blessing."

Working on NDT in the nuclear industry clearly suited Turnbow's love of learning and doing new things. "You've got innovations all the time. While working at TVA, we ended up with a group of about 130 people performing chemistry, calibrations, nondestructive testing, quality assurance, metallurgy, and instrumentation engineering. We touched everything that went on inside TVA, the largest federal utility in the country. We had fifty-nine fossil units, seven nuclear units, twenty-something hydros, and a whole bunch of gas units. When that equipment was running, it was also developing maintenance problems – materials were wearing out, things were being replaced, and needed inspection, so we saw and did many different things."

CHANGING JOBS WHEN NECESSARY

After a while, the boom of building nuclear power plants was over. "The demand for power started to decline, so we had to start backing off." TVA canceled some plants. Of the original planned seventeen, ten nuclear units were cancelled. Thus came the end of the building era. "As construction slowed, I wanted to get back to Chattanooga, and I tried to transfer within TVA, but I didn't get to. The company wanted to keep me where I was."

Determined to return to Chattanooga, Turnbow sought out the world's largest pressure vessel manufacturer, Combustion Engineering (C-E), headquartered where he wanted to be located.

"It was like, if you've ever dreamed of going into a professional sport and playing for a certain team, it would be that team. This company had a huge reputation. They were building pressure vessels and nuclear reactors to be shipped all over the world, including to the U.S. Navy. Some of the reactors were built to power navy carriers such as the Washington, the Lincoln, and the Reagan. During this time, and by a stroke of luck, the C-E NDT Level III left the company in pursuit of another job. So they hired me."

Turnbow was motivated to excel and soon. "I had to go to Pittsburgh and take a test to show I knew what I was doing. The track record is that many fail the test the first time. So they set me up to expect an initial failure. They give you the books to study, so I didn't quite understand that failure rate," Turnbow explained.

"I was determined to pass the test, so I studied hard. I also went to talk to the DCAS (Defense Contract Administrative Service) inspectors who oversee the Navy work. They were experienced people, and they would help me if I didn't understand what was in the codes and the manuals. Anyway, I passed the test the first time. It was a big day for me – Combustion wasn't used to folks passing without a second try. It made me feel good. My advice – if there is a challenge before you, don't take it lightly. The testing in this business is the last safety net. You must always take it seriously because the decisions you make have huge consequences."

THE JOB OF MAKING SURE THINGS ARE RIGHT

On the job, Level I is made up of trainees or new people; Level II are the people who perform the inspections, gather the data, record it, and hand it up the line; Turnbow's level, Level III, the Engineering Group, manages the inspections.

"The Engineering Group has to deal with the nonconformances—things that aren't right. Sometimes it gets exciting, since it's our job to find the flaws which may end up as million-dollar repairs. I remember one major repair – the result of a bad welding process – and unfortunately we only caught the flaw at the end of fabrication. It had never happened before, and here I was, twenty-nine years old, the new guy walking into the shop, doing ultrasonic testing on these welds, and I had to say they were bad. I spent two or three days agonizing over it, verifying, re-verifying, making sure I was right, because I knew what it was going to take to fix it."

Turnbow's skills would be put to the test, literally.

"The Navy admiral came down from Washington, and all the top management came to the shop to watch. The Navy brought in this big round piece of pipe welded to a nozzle and told us they were going to cut out a piece of the metal with a grinder to sample the metal for a flaw. Then they would put red dye on the metal, let it soak up, wipe it off, and then put white developer over it. If the metal really had cracked, the dye would bleed out of the developer."

During the testing, "I was holding my breath; I didn't know you could hold your breath for thirty minutes, but it's possible. I knew I was turning blue," Turnbow laughs. "They ground it out, put the dye on it, sprayed the white stuff, and, as I'm standing there watching, it bled all over the place. The admiral looked right at me and said, 'Fine job, son.' My management just looked at me with a slight smile and I was so relieved. NDT had done its job – found the flaw – and now it would be removed."

The point, Turnbow says, "is that your integrity is paramount. Your decision-making has to be perfect. You can be wrong and make errors, but it should never be the result of shoddy work or fear of the results. You get the data, you analyze it the way you've been taught, and hopefully you've been taught correctly, and then you make the call. If it goes against production and profits, so be it. You didn't put the flaw in there, somebody else did, so you have to tell yourself, 'This is what I do,' and plant your feet and insist it be taken care of."

This concern for safety, Turnbow notes, holds true for all industries. "I've basically always been in nuclear, but think about planes, trains, and bridges. Is there any difference? People's lives are affected, at any one moment, all the time. The inspection of airplanes and nuclear power plants is huge. We even inspect food. So it doesn't matter which industry you get in, you have to take this business seriously; there's nothing light about it. There will always be safety concerns for workers, but, on the nuclear side, the concern is for both the workers and the public. In other industries, safety may not be a concern, but worries about systems going offline and the company not making money. You've got to be a businessman at least a little bit, but you've got to put your safety hat on first. If everything is going to be safe, you've got to fix the problem component."

Still, Turnbow acknowledges, "You need to have fun with whatever you do. I did. I didn't know anything about nuclear, but I thought it was going to be fun. And it has probably exceeded anything I ever dreamed of because, as we say in Middle Tennessee, we were plowing new ground my whole career."

Turnbow did well at Combustion Engineering. "I became the manager of the department with around 100 or 110 employees in the different groups who worked for me over there. I had just turned thirty when I got that job."

At that point, the company was actually shrinking. A lot of work had been going overseas for years, and Combustion was fighting to survive.

"That's another problem you'll face sometimes," Turnbow warns. "Industries go up and down. In this country, that trend keeps getting worse. I don't care what you do these days. To stay employed, you're going to have to travel, and change jobs quite a bit. However, I've heard it said that Nondestructive Examination (NDE) is recession-proof. Over all the years, and with all the recessions we've had, the Hutchinson Vocational School in Minnesota has been graduating students in NDT for over thirty years and claims to have a 100-percent placement rate. Not bad!"

Things at Combustion starting drying up and Turnbow ended up back at TVA, managing the inspection and testing the TVA's power plant fleet. Over the years, other responsibilities were added to his job description including metallurgy, chemistry, calibration services, and instrumentation engineering services. Each of these brought more challenges.

"Materials in any kind of operating equipment, whether it be a car, an airplane, a coal, gas, or nuclear plant, whatever, are going to wear out or set up a degradation mechanism. In the nuclear power industry these things were built to last; they're heavy, and overdesigned. They have redundant systems so, if one goes out, another one kicks in. But every now and then, the chemistry and the makeup of the particular material breaks down for some reason. It wasn't supposed to, but it did. There's never a boring moment during the day. You don't get to sit back and relax and enjoy the success when things are working, because you've got to go back and look at something else that isn't.

"The worst case, the one that surprised me the most, was when a degradation mechanism developed in stainless steel, in other words the material started to crack. It's supposed to last forever. The degradation was detected in the '80s when some pipes failed. We were going along thinking everything was fine, but NDT had missed these flaws. So this was one of those stressful moments."

A breakdown of the metal—intergranular stress corrosion cracking or IGSCC—was occurring in this material and NDT had missed it.

"It attacked the plant at Nine Mile Point in '82. They had just finished an in-service inspection, and they started up the plant and ran for a while. Well, the pipe cracked and leaked on the floor. That set off our first alarm that something wasn't right. So we reacted to the leak with the NRC, cut the pipe out, used it as a mock-up, and started trying to find out how and why people missed it. Then we set up a qualification test, a demo, where everybody had to prove they could find these flaws. The process worked pretty well, as the NDT examinations stopped missing the flaw. A few years later, another material, alloy 600, did the same thing. It failed, and flaws were missed again."

Turnbow stresses flaws are usually related to the age of the metal and the temperature it endures.

He says, "Pacific Northwest Laboratory serves as a consultant to the NRC on NDT matters, and their top guy, Steve Doctor (who really is a doctor, so he's Doctor Doctor), wrote a paper on the performance of NDE. In it, he pointed out NDE has not been able to get on the front end of failure mechanisms and catch them until there is water on the floor. That resonated well and led a group of us to approach the problem head-on."

THE NEED FOR SOLID TRAINING PROGRAMS

The incident at Three Mile Island in 1979 became an impetus for Turnbow's commitment to ensuring nuclear technicians are properly trained and prepared to deal with anything that might happen.

According to Turnbow, "Three Mile Island happened because the operators were not trained properly. There was a major congressional study to see what went wrong. They discussed the flawed procedures and commented that the individuals at the site had no idea what to do when multiple things occurred simultaneously. If only one event happened, all was good. But on that day, multiple things went wrong and they lost it. They just didn't know what to do."

Turnbow says, "Today, operators can't walk out of a training simulator until they deal with multiple failures, and they know exactly what they need to do. I've got chills right now. The nuclear industry's commitment to doing it right!'"

He admits having so many things fail at once is a rarity. "But the exact same thing had happened at another utility down the road from Three Mile Island only a few months earlier. But that site was at low power starting up. They were able to turn back from any mistakes. But Three Mile Island was at high power. Unfortunately, at that time, Three Mile Island was unable to learn from the other utility's mistakes. Today there is a system in place to ensure information is shared and mistakes are not repeated."

Ultimately, the Three Mile Island plant was cooled down and no one got hurt. But it was a close call and the reactor was rendered unusable. People in the U.S. started to turn against nuclear power.

"It set us back," Turnbow acknowledged. "And it wasn't until the 2000s that we were able to start up nuclear power sites. There are numerous new nuclear units in construction right now—two at VC Summer, and two at Vogtle. Also, TVA is completing a new plant at Watts Bar and should start up in late 2015. It will be the first new nuclear plant completed and started up in this century."

CREATING A SYSTEM FOR TRAINING

In 1995, Turnbow became president of the American Society for Nondestructive Testing (ASNT). "On my first day as president, I went into the board of directors meeting and said we have to address these failures. The story was building that there was something wrong in the industry. I said we need a million dollars to build a performance-based certification program where people can demonstrate their competence in finding flaws. Up until then, we were kind of training people one-on-one every time something failed. So I suggested we train the workforce up front so they all know what they're doing beforehand instead of dealing with each failure as it occurred."

The system before had been employer-based – employers were free to train their people any way they wished, and there were no standards. "We grew up in that method and hadn't ever thought about it. It was the way we did it," explains Turnbow. "A lot of us had begun to realize it didn't make any sense. So we built this program in a single year (from '96 to '97) and put it on the market. It was slow catching on. Employers were reluctant to try it since it was not required by regulators or code. We tried to get the support of the ASME (American Society for Mechanical Engineers), but there was a resistance to change."

To establish credibility, Turnbow's group finally talked ASNT into allowing an audit in the year 2006; there were twenty-seven audit findings—none was a significant issue to address.

He notes that twenty-seven isn't a big deal. "The program was new, and ASNT just wasn't following its own procedures—everybody does stuff like that from time to time and then gets better as audits point out issues. But what got us is we couldn't get them to close the audit—address the issues. This seemed very strange to me. Here we were, the world's largest nondestructive testing society, and we're just trying to get these audit findings closed. When this was discussed with the NDT community, everybody just looked confused. It was amazing."

He continued, "We let it go for eighteen months. In 2008, I was the chairman of the Electric Power Research Institute Nondestructive Examination (EPRI NDE) Center in Charlotte, North Carolina. The NDE center exists for nuclear; they do research and development. The IGSCC and the alloy 600 issue I mentioned, including thermal fatigue, all the testing was there, and we, the utility industry, built the tests. We were the right people at the right place to say, 'Look, we've got demonstrations, we're trying to verify people know what they're doing, but we haven't even thought about training them.' What could we do at this point? We were hearing over and over the workers weren't prepared, and those being tested had a fifty-percent failure rate. By 2008, we realized ASNT would not pass the audit, we'd let it just sit out there for eighteen months, it was time we moved on and created something that worked!"

The EPRI NDE Center committee dealing with this issue had thirty-five utility members—thirty-two voted for Turnbow's proposal, one voted against, and there were two abstentions. Turnbow took it as a powerful message, "Go forth and do it! So I left them, went to New York, met with the American Society of Mechanical Engineers. The industry volunteers of this organization write the codes to which we build our nuclear plants. We were asking them to help us create a new qualification and certification program. At first they said, 'We don't do that,' but after they truly considered it, they changed their minds and said, 'Okay, we're in, we're going to do it.'"

In 2010, the ASME board of directors voted for Turnbow and his team who created the program. Turnbow knew there were good practices out there already. He was particularly interested in one known as Systematic Approach to Training (SAT), which came out of World War II. "When the U.S. was trying to build airplanes, we couldn't get them off the ground fast enough and the quality was poor. So the government challenged the industry to develop better training."

The training approach that came out of it was, at the core, "a system of how to train and provide constant feedback to fix things. Whatever you kept finding wrong, you kept fixing it. If there was weakness in the training and people were making mistakes over and over, you kept fixing the training until everything worked. That's how the SAT process improved the quality and production of U.S. planes during World War II."

The SAT process starts with a job task analysis to find out what the job's all about; qualification cards (qual-cards) are used to evaluate the skills required, which are verified by a subject matter expert. Once the training is done and the documentation is complete, the trainee takes the appropriate test.

Turnbow says, "We were on our way to building our own system from scratch with an organization that didn't do non-destructive testing. They develop codes and standards to build pressure vessels for gas, oil, as well as nuclear. We created a committee and then went looking for money. We got about 700,000 dollars from utilities and the Nuclear Regulatory Commission, which was concerned about NDE performance, but we needed $2.5 million. So we started beating the bushes for money, looking for grants."

The project was going well, but Turnbow and his ANDE team were running out of money. They then leveraged Chattanooga State Community College's ability to qualify for grants and capitalized on ASME's name and worldwide membership—seventy countries and 140,000 members.

The partnership was forged, and, ultimately they were able to land a $1.5 million grant to add to the $700,000 they already had. That brought them to $2.2 million, still $300,000 short of the funds needed. But Turnbow was determined to succeed!

"I said, I'll throw a rock and hit it from here, and we'll make it, we're going to make it. The moral of the story here is, if you don't have enough money, and you ask for more, they keep giving it to you, and you keep spending it. If there isn't any money, and you know you're not going to get anymore, you make it work with what you have." So Turnbow got everything done for the $2.2 million.

It wasn't Turnbow alone who did the work. "The ANDE committee included eighteen members, so, when I say 'my program,' I really mean 'our' program – all eighteen of us. We started out trying to reinvent the NDE training qualification certification process. We studied the Three Mile Island incident, the resulting INPO training process and realized we were surrounded by the solution. We didn't need to invent anything. We just needed to find out what existed and what was needed and include the very best practices."

The training program for nuclear is almost completed. Turnbow boasts a bit, "It's not anything you've ever seen before in my industry, the new standard—ANDE-1. It's got all the stuff in it that the nuclear industry uses for all other nuclear power plant workers. Now we're going to be able sit in front of the NRC and say we're like them now, we're like those high performers who never mess up anymore."

This hasn't quite happened yet. Turnbow admits, "In the last ten years, we've missed over twenty flaws that leaked into the nuclear power plant. Info. on most of these events is available to the public through NRC public meetings and posted on the NRC ADAMS website. But some of the utilities are starting to get very concerned about a big one happening. So we've been racing to get this done and implemented to make sure it does not happen again."

He says, "This year we published a new NDE performance-based ASME standard (ANDE-1). It includes qual-cards and job task analysis. In fact, it's got everything the employer-based system doesn't have. It's centralized, and we're using The Institute for Nuclear Power Operation's best practices and psychometrics for written and practical tests.

"I had the good fortune of being part of the ASME when the group decided we needed to do something different. It's now called the ANDE/ASME Non-Destructive Examination program. As I approach the end of my career, my dream to improve the performance of NDE is actually coming true!"

COMMITMENT TO HIGHER EDUCATION

While working on the training program, Turnbow was also involved in building an associate's degree program at Chattanooga State Community College.

"Everything I've shared regarding the training is designed for high school grads who get a certificate to do the technician's work. We had a little strategy there. We were going to cover it all – training at all levels – and we built the Cadillac first (the NDE Associated Degree Program), and then we employed what was applicable and built a certificate program."

Today this is the only college with an NDE program that is accredited by the Accreditation Board for Engineering and Technology (ABET) in the U.S. There's not another one in the country.

LOOKING BACK ON HIS CAREER

Turnbow has other achievements to be proud of, aside from spearheading the change in how technicians are trained.

"When I was promoted to manager of the Inspection Services Organization (ISO) in TVA in the early 1990s, my team had been nominated for a Hammer Award [then-Vice President Gore's Hammer Award offers recognition to teams of federal employees whose work resulted in a government that works better and costs less]. We were one of the first federal organizations to receive this award with Vice President Al Gore traveling to Tennessee to personally present this honor. Needless to say, the ISO organization was flying high."

His management style had a lot to do with his success. All of his people were union workers. He went to his workers, who were sure they were about to be laid off, and told them they had a reprieve.

"Unfortunately, they had grievances over everything. They had more grievances than any other organization inside TVA. I told them, 'You've got to get rid of that. If you have a problem, come see me—I'll solve it with you. They're not going to let us stay if we're a constant problem.'"

The moral of that story? Turnbow says, "You work together, management and employees. I had promised them forever more, 'If you have a problem, my door is always open. You come to me, you bring your union steward, I don't care, and we'll get the book out, and we'll solve the problem, deal?' Every one of their grievances went away that day. And, from that day forward, I've never had another one."

For the next twenty-two years, all grievances were settled within the department; none had to go to arbitration.

One last thing Turnbow wants to share is his commitment to providing simulators to help nuclear industry technicians get the experience they need to keep themselves and the public safe. As the standards were being codified and the training program was approaching completion, he noted ASNT documents stated technicians needed three months of experience. But it didn't specify anything beyond the minimum experience requirement.

"Now, the new ANDE program mandates that you've got to have a qual-card to tell you what you need to be able to do, and that a subject matter expert [SME or Level III] has to sign off on the qual-card. But where are we going to send these people to get the right experience? There's hardly any manufacturing in the U.S. anymore and very little construction. So how do you get people into manufacturing and construction? Will any company pay them a salary while they are in training? Any way you look at it, it is not working. This dilemma has existed for over ten years as we have tried to grow a new workforce as baby boomers approached retirement."

His team started talking about simulation. "About two years ago," Turnbow recalls, "I went to Disney World with my kids and grandkids. And I thought to myself, I've got to find out how they do these simulations. And it isn't just Disney. There are lots of simulations out there."

Turnbow was impressed by Disney's simulations. "They can simulate a room on the computer, and you will think you're in it."

But he acknowledges the nuclear industry doesn't need that level of complexity. "Here's a long story short," he said. "We had a little bit of the grant money left at the end of the training project, and we took some of it to start building these online training materials. We spent about $70,000 of ASME's money to create a simulator proof of concept, and it worked! We took data off an NDE machine with real flaws in it, and we were able to download it from the web and simulate it on the computer as if it were real.

"Then, we received another gift from God. This guy on my committee—the chairman of the ANDE subcommittee on training—called and told me he ran across this Canadian guy in Argentina who wanted to show me his training, because he thinks he's has what I was looking for. So he came to Chattanooga State Community College.

"He fired up his computer, threw projected images up on the wall, and displayed metal that depicted a piece of plate, a transducer, and realistic sounds. He had built an animation that included real flaws and it was impressive! He then showed me the evaluation. I saw a weld, a piece of pipe, and flaws in it. He scanned over the flaws, and the screen danced like crazy, just like in real life."

Turnbow asked if those were real flaws. "Absolutely," was the response.

"No," Turnbow replied. "You've got to understand what I'm asking you. Are those real flaws? Did you transmit the flaws out of a piece of pipe, bring them over, and am I looking at a real flaw?"

Again the response was, "Absolutely."

This had been a dream for Turnbow. "This man was developing this simulator all by himself, using his own money. He had sold a company that sells NDE equipment, and he knew there was a void in the training, which was the same problem we were working on here. And he told me he personally wanted to fix it, explaining, 'I had plenty of money, so I have spent the past three years working on this.'"

Turnbow and some of the other members of his committee felt this was incredible. "We all started dreaming about this three years ago. We've chased grants trying to get money to build this. We've found people who say they know how to do it. We had three people with three different skill sets working on it, and now we find all this capability rolled up into this one guy. He had already built the basic simulator and it actually exceeded our expectations. This was one of those events you have to call a gift. Yes, a gift from God."

This amazing expert will return as Turnbow and his team are running their classes, and they will conduct a beta test on his invention. So, in conjunction with the traditional class work, the students are going to get a backup dose of knowledge via the simulation. Turnbow is excited and optimistic about this new simulator technology.

During his career, Turnbow has had frustrations, but even more successes. He has enjoyed all of it. To those interested in a career in the nuclear industry, he offers this encouragement. "The journey through this industry has been incredible, I highly recommend it. And it's still in its infancy; it's still a baby. The technology is now really getting interesting because it's going very fast and changing the way we do business by producing more data and making the evaluation of the data easier. We have a shortage of inspectors, with wages creeping up, so it's a good place to make a good living. If you don't want to have an associate's degree, and you wanted to go straight into getting certified, this program requires a high school diploma, or a GED."

"You have to have a mind for math and science because trigonometry and geometry are used in triangulating, locating those flaws. But if the industry sounds interesting, and you're looking for a challenge, the nuclear industry could be a great place for you."

LESSONS LEARNED

- There are many challenges in nuclear jobs. You can't take them lightly because other people's safety relies on your willingness to learn and meet those challenges head-on.

- You can't trade off profit for safety when people's lives are at stake.

- Be confident in your training. You must be willing to make hard decisions based on careful testing and consideration.

- Do not take for granted that things work as they were intended. Even the most durable parts can break.

CHAPTER 8

◆

CHERI D. COLLINS

Southern Company General Manager, Nuclear Operations
and Development

*After training, the employee returns to his job and goes into the
field to perform a task, and in so doing so, discovers his training
was deficient. If there is no mechanism to plow that knowledge
back into the training material, then the knowledge dies with
that person, and the training program continues to teach a deficient methodology to other students.*

IN THE YEAR 2000, CHERI COLLINS HAD BEEN ON THE JOB AS AN
operations manager at the Joseph M. Farley Nuclear Power
Plant for a mere six months, but with her eighteen years of
experience in all aspects of operating the nuclear power plant,
she felt confident their training program was effective and up-
to-date.

"There was some naiveté associated with my newness as a manager," she says, "but we took our training program seriously, and I believed it was in good shape."

After spending the afternoon briefing members of the Institute of Nuclear Power Operations Accrediting Board, she was no less confident. Collins spent the night in an Atlanta hotel with little to fragment her sleep. However, the next morning, "INPO's Vice President of Training & Accreditation called our Vice-President to say, 'We're placing your program on probation.' I felt sick to my stomach," she says.

"That was such a wake-up call, not just for me, but all my bosses who preceded me," she says. "We just didn't have a thorough understanding of the important role of training to improve performance. During our six-month probation period, we worked very hard and very close with the INPO representative assigned to coach us through the corrective actions we needed to take."

After the probationary period and a return visit to the Accrediting Board, they got the "all-clear" for their operations training program. "This process demands that you understand 'what went wrong,' then put together a clear-cut plan to fix it, and prevent it from happening again." In the case of Farley's program, "one of our more significant issues was our failure to evaluate the training's effectiveness. That is the last step in the SAT- based process (Systematic Approach to Training) and is important because it gives the student a mechanism to provide feedback to improve the training," she says.

Collins explains, "Let's say I teach an employee how to take a certain mechanism apart and put it back together again. I teach the employee using written material, and perhaps, even hands-on training with a mock-up. After training, the employee returns to his job and goes into the field to perform this very task, and in doing so, discovers his training was deficient and had not fully prepared him for the task. If there is no mechanism to plow that knowledge back into the training material, then the knowledge dies with that person, and the training program continues to teach a deficient methodology to other students."

THE FUNDAMENTALS OF TRAINING

"In the high-stakes realm of nuclear power plant operation, the training must be effective enough to ensure any qualified operator can perform any function he or she is trained on, regardless of the pressure," Collins says.

"If there is a human performance error in the field, the first question you must ask—this is the acid test—if I had put the proverbial gun to John's head, would he have been able to perform the task correctly? If the answer is no, then there is a training problem—you have to get at those seeds of ineffective training. Training is fundamental to excellence in human performance."

The INPO process is thorough, Collins says. "They come in to assess your training program—several evaluators—and dive into every crevasse—like ants on shortbread."

The plant provides its own assessment of the adequacy of its training programs, but the INPO inspectors don't take the plant's assessment at face value, Collins says. "They come in and check every jot and tittle, and make their own observations."

Then, at INPO headquarters in Atlanta, key people from the plant's management are brought in to defend their program. "You go before the Accrediting Board with members of senior plant management, the manager of the department being assessed for accreditation renewal, and the Training manager. It's very, very formal—everyone is dressed to the nines—the board questions and drills down and questions some more," Collins says.

The Nuclear Training Accrediting Board is typically composed of representatives from academia, such as a professor from an engineering school, high-level peers from other plants, and a representative from the NRC. The chairman is usually the chief executive officer from a different utility company. 'This board is determined to make sure you've got a program that can take a person who doesn't know a pump from a valve and train them to be a first-class nuclear professional who can work in a nuclear plant and get the job done absolutely right the first time," she says.

ACCREDITATION AND WATERSHED EVENTS

Since then, Collins has participated in other INPO accreditation review boards and passed. Collins herself served fifteen months as a loaned employee to INPO.

She and other officials at the Joseph M. Farley Nuclear Plant had learned their lessons about the importance of training and applied those lessons learned to the other training programs—maintenance, engineering, chemistry, and health physics.

"Just as Three Mile Island was a watershed event for the entire U.S. nuclear power industry (more about that later), operations training probation was a watershed for our plant,' she says. "We had not implemented all the steps of the systematic approach to training. We did not have the necessary respect for training as the chief mechanism to improve human performance."

"The levels and layers of review for operating a nuclear power plant have been developed to cover any contingency—from an earthquake to acts of terror," she says. "But the key to operating a safe and secure plant always comes down to dedicated, well- trained, qualified people—the people you work with and work for."

When she first went into the nuclear field in the early 1980s, Collins was admittedly puzzled by the endless, seemingly pointless redundancies and strict procedures. Then one day, quite suddenly, she says, it all made sense. "You're not making toothpaste or selling dog food, though we appreciate people who do that—you're splitting atoms. That was key for understanding the rigor and demanding nature of the business.

"When I became a manager, it dawned on me when I spoke to our employees, I needed them to understand that in reality they didn't work for me, or my boss, or even our CEO. They worked for the people who lived in the area, who drove by the plant every day on their way to wherever, and had no clue what went on inside that fence, and had all of their fingers and toes crossed hoping we knew what we were doing. The plant's neighbors, that's who you work for."

SUMMER JOB

At the start of her career, a nuclear family, rather than nuclear power, was closer to the top of her agenda. Collins had graduated from the University of Alabama at Birmingham with a degree in civil engineering. "My sole focus was finding a good job!"

She worked as a summer student engineer with the Alabama Power Company in a district office in 1978, but post-graduation, in 1982, "the job market was quite slow." A connection from her first job out of college in the natural gas industry led to an interview with the Farley plant, but she'd never seriously considered a career in nuclear power.

And the feeling was mutual. "No one had envisioned there might one day be women working at the plant," she says. It was quite a cultural adjustment, for both employee and employer.

Four years into her tenure at Farley, she was offered the opportunity to attend reactor operator training, a grueling, sixteen-month course that culminated in the attainment of her Senior Reactor Operator License. Operator licenses are granted by the NRC after successful completion of written exams, simulator exams, and plant walk-throughs.

"That was the hardest thing I've ever done. It was four years of work rolled into sixteen months," she says. "You're in class every day. You're learning reactor theory, the ins and outs of the plant, emergency procedures, technical specifications, how each piece of equipment is supposed to perform in multiple scenarios. You're practicing responses to scenarios on a simulator, which replicates the control room in every detail."

The extremely thorough training to become a reactor operator derived, in part, because of an event that has cast a shadow over nuclear power, with profound consequences that continue to impact the industry today.

Collins came into her career shortly after the partial meltdown of the Three Mile Island reactor near Harrisburg, Pennsylvania, on March 28, 1979. "It was a watershed event. There were no injuries nor adverse health effects, and the small amount of radioactive gas released was not enough to cause any dose above background levels to the public," she says. "There was less radioactive dose associated with the release than you would get during a dental exam." However, the event galvanized resistance to nuclear energy, and many new plant projects were shelved.

The event was caused by a combination of equipment malfunction and human error, but began with an equipment malfunction in the form of a stuck-open relief valve; an operator then mistakenly overrode the emergency cooling system, preventing vital cooling water from being delivered to the core. Over time, the lack of core cooling led to the partial meltdown of the nuclear fuel. Inspectors determined a valve position indicator light, hidden by poor control board design from the operators' sight, also contributed to the event. The cleanup took fourteen years and cost $1 billion.

There were plenty of lessons learned for the plants that were still operating. Among them were that plant officials had little to no training on how to explain such events—calmly, clearly, and accurately—to the media, which was the primary source of information for an alarmed public.

"We learned we needed training in order to respond to questions from the media, giving them accurate information in a way a non-nuclear professional could understand it," she says. "We also learned to work closely and collegially with local and state agencies in our shared priority to communicate with and protect the public."

"When you say the word 'leak,' the public jumps way out there, and there's no need for it. You have to be honest and very succinct in your explanations. Timely updates are an important factor for the plant's credibility—and clear expectations for restoring the plant must also be communicated," Collins says.

"Although TMI resulted in a partial meltdown of the nuclear fuel in the core, the reason there was no harm to the public was the design of the plant," Collins says. "It is designed to minimize radiation exposure to the public, even with a core meltdown."

Design criteria are set by the NRC and are followed strictly during all phases of construction. You don't sidestep it, and you don't lobby your way around it."

She explains, "The human error contribution to the Three Mile Island event was caused by inadequate emergency response training—period. Those operators had not received the training necessary to understand the event that was unfolding before their eyes."

Her ability to communicate clear explanations of complex, nuclear power plant design aspects is part natural inclination and part training.

Among Collins' many roles in the nuclear power industry over the past thirty-two years was her position as spokesperson for Georgia Power's new reactor construction in Augusta, Georgia where she was tasked with explaining technical issues to laymen. She has been a "face and voice" of nuclear energy in the South for decades.

"We have two independent entities to hold us accountable. First and foremost is the Nuclear Regulatory Commission. (I wish the natural gas and oil industry were governed by an equivalent agency.) The public doesn't understand the rigor by which a nuclear plant is first designed and constructed, and then operated and maintained," Collins says. "Although the NRC has given me many headaches over the years, I wouldn't change a thing. It's their sole mission to protect the health and safety of the public, and they do that extremely well. On the other hand, INPO, the Institute of Nuclear Power Operations, is an organization that drives the industry toward excellence. It is a non-profit organization composed of permanent employees and augmented with employees "on loan" from various nuclear plants across the country. Many of my colleagues spent fifteen months to two years in "on-loan" assignments with INPO."

INPO establishes performance objectives and conducts regular, detailed evaluations of all aspects of plant operations. The evaluations may well include findings that detail where plant performance is falling short of the excellence mark. The plant must respond to the findings with corrective actions that not only take care of the issue but also prevent it from recurring.

Every two years, each plant receives a thorough evaluation, which culminates in a rating of INPO 1 through INPO 5. Every plant strives to be an INPO 1—the representation of excellence in all aspects of plant operations. Each year there is an awards ceremony. The utility CEOs representing INPO 1 plants are recognized during the ceremony to receive their plants' award of excellence. Of course, CEOs are proud of their plants, and all are hopeful for an INPO 1 award; this helps them push for excellence across the board.

Collins adds "INPO has definitely improved the industry by setting high standards for the plants—and the good ole' fashioned peer pressure hasn't hurt anything, either."

For Collins, much of the satisfaction during her career came from "making real connections with the employees" she says. "Most of my employees were men and I think the reason they accepted me was because I made it clear I both respected their skill and their dedication and I had their best interests at heart."

"And so for the next generation, as well, I know the kind of money you can make is outstanding, but the real reward is being a part of something that constantly works on improvement with a goal of becoming excellent. It is intoxicating."

"Occasionally, I have had the pleasure of addressing young people who are finishing high school or college and are entertaining the idea of a career in nuclear energy." she says. "I always tell them, it is a lot of hard work and a lot of pressure. It demands you live an alcohol-responsible and a drug-free lifestyle, so if you cannot commit to that, then don't bother. But if you enjoy being associated with something that will always demand your best self, and in the process make you a part of something extraordinary, then nuclear energy just might be for you."

LESSONS LEARNED

■ Redundancies in procedures are largely responsible for the nuclear power industry's remarkable safety record.

■ The public's perception of human error in the nuclear power industry is of paramount importance to the growth of the nuclear energy industry.

■ The nuclear energy industry has stringent oversight from multiple agencies to ensure high universal quality and safety standards.

■ Training is fundamental to excellence in human performance.

CHAPTER 9

◆

ROBERT SINGLETERRY, PhD

Nuclear Engineer, NASA

The nuclear engineering community—in fact, the entire nuclear industry—is small. People move around but often come back into your life at the most unexpected times.

EXPLORING THE OPTIONS

IN HIGH SCHOOL, ROBERT SINGLETERRY WAS A SELF-PROFESSED GEEK. "I took five years of math and five years of science in four years of high school. I took everything from algebra to calculus, from physical science all the way up to physics."

Like most teenagers, Singleterry often changed his mind about what he wanted to do with the rest of his life. "I wanted to be Carl Sagan or, at least, one of his students. I wanted to be a cosmologist. I thought it would be fascinating and exciting."

But his parents wanted him to be realistic, pointing out that most cosmologists make very little money. To this day, there are fewer than 1,000 cosmologists in the world who actually make a comfortable living. After all, Singleterry points out, "Neil deGrasse Tyson has said, 'I don't make a lot of money; why do you think I'm on TV?'"

So he switched his aspirations to acting. "After they stopped laughing, they told me, 'Not on our dime!' So that dream went out the window." For a while, he thought about being an orthodontist, mostly because he knew they made a lot of money. But after interning with his own orthodontist, who showed him firsthand that orthodontics can be very boring, he changed his mind. "He told me to make a choice – money or interesting. I chose interesting."

His parents suggested engineering, but Singleterry told them he preferred nuclear physics because it sounded more interesting. He explains, "One of the great things about my high school is they brought in experts from different industries to talk to the students. One of these experts was a guy named Morris Farr, who came to talk to my chemistry class. He was talking about his research in fusion energy, and a couple of us got really excited about that."

FOLLOWING THE NUCLEAR ENGINEERING PATH
Singleterry followed up on his burgeoning interest in nuclear physics by visiting the University of Arizona (UA) physics department to see what it might offer him upon graduation. But the prospects were daunting. "The department was huge," he says. "I would have just been a number, not an individual. No one would care about me." But Farr, the expert who had come to his chemistry class, taught in the nuclear engineering department at UA, which was a much smaller department. Singleterry thought, "Hey, why not? I liked the word nuclear, and I liked the look of mushroom clouds."

He was in the program for about a week when he realized one of his professors was Norman Hilberry, a pioneer in the nuclear industry and the first "SCRAM." (In the original reactor created in 1942 by Enrico Fermi, there was a control rod that was spring-loaded. Fermi had an acronym: SCRAM—safety control rod axe man. To shut down the reactor, he pointed to this "SCRAM," who would chop through a rope and "spring" the control rod into the reactor.) Hilberry later became the second director of the Argonne National Laboratory, the successor to the Manhattan Project. He retired to Arizona, got bored, came to the university, and asked if he could teach.

Singleterry was impressed that such a historical figure was teaching the freshman class in nuclear engineering.

It actually took Singleterry five years to finish up the four-year nuclear engineering bachelor's program. This was because, as in high school, he took advantage of every opportunity to explore other potential careers. He thought seriously about going on to medical school to become a doctor, spending a year taking biology, organic chemistry, and other courses on that scholastic path. He volunteered at the nuclear medicine department at the university's medical school while still working on the nuclear engineering curriculum. But realizing he didn't want to be an M.D., he returned his focus to nuclear engineering.

Even then, he kept investigating his chosen field to learn everything he could. He notes being a nuclear engineer requires a serious commitment. "I talked to many people, went to numerous American Nuclear Society meetings. Back then, nuclear was popular, people were spending a lot of money, and they were interested in young people entering the nuclear field, so they were more than happy to talk to me. I was part of the next generation."

The extra course work resulted in the extra year as an undergraduate, but Singleterry doesn't regret it. "By exploring different options, I was able to eliminate professions that would have been wrong for me," he says, noting it is as important to know what you don't want to do, as it is to know what you do want to do. Singleterry stuck with the nuclear engineering major, but admits his road wasn't always easy. "It's a long, torturous process—you don't just wake up and become an engineer," he warns those entering the field. But when he graduated in May of 1984, he knew it was worth it.

After finishing his degree, he considered going on to graduate school at Purdue. But, after five years of college, Singleterry was weary of classrooms, so he accepted a position as a reactor engineer at Georgia Power's E.I. Hatch nuclear power plant in Baxley. There was a glut of nuclear engineers out looking for jobs because the nearby Zimmer plant had closed, but Singleterry was hired because he indicated on his resumé that he knew how to run the VAX/VMS system from Digital Equipment Company, which they used at the university. Georgia Power had just acquired a VAX to do the data extraction and data analysis for their GE boiling water reactor. Wanting a backup computer person on staff who knew what was going on, the company sent Singleterry to Digital Equipment School to get trained. "All in all," he says, "it was a nice entry-level job."

At the time, Singleterry's wife, also a UA nuclear engineering graduate, was hired as an operator of an advanced test reactor at an Idaho nuclear plant. Singleterry thought now might be a good time to take another look at grad school. He looked up the professor he had consulted with at Purdue and told him he wanted to do work in fusion. "I wanted to build the next nuclear power plant," Singleterry says. The Purdue representative said the research he'd be doing for graduate work would be on plasma. "I wanted to build a fusion reactor. But he said we were fifty years from achieving that!"

He decided grad school could wait.

SIDELINED INTO SOFTWARE INTEGRATION

Singleterry had graduated from UA in May 1984, and started at Georgia Power in August of that year. But his tenure was short. After about seven months, his wife went to Idaho for her new job. Looking for a job closer to his wife, he interviewed with a company called EI (not the same as the E.I. Hatch nuclear power plant). The company had developed the RETRAN system, which did thermal-hydraulic analyses of nuclear reactors.

This was right after the Three Mile Island incident and the government required every reactor to have a safety parameter display system (SPDS). Singleterry explains an SPDS could take a whole range of the plant parameters, which would allow operators to learn what was happening throughout the plant on a single display. "That's what went wrong at Three Mile Island," he says. "The operators didn't have a single view of what was going wrong, and a single person couldn't diagnose it and arrange to fix it." At Three Mile Island, many things went wrong at once, but no one person knew all that was happening. So the Nuclear Regulatory Commission's response was to require an SPDS.

Singleterry was perfect for EI's needs at the time. The company was having a problem integrating the fuel warranty system to the SPDS system they were building for the GE boiling water reactor at the James A. Fitzpatrick Nuclear Generating Station in Oswego, N.Y. Part of the system was running fuel warranty software from GE, and "they didn't understand what was happening with the GE stuff," he says. The EI personnel didn't know how to integrate that software with their display system.

Singleterry had just spent nine months doing the same thing at Georgia Power with the same GE software. He interviewed with EI on Friday and was asked if he could start on Monday. This gave him a well-paying job doing software integration for nuclear reactions, and was a fine choice until he made a decision about graduate school. EI was made up primarily of computer scientists, and Singleterry was the only nuclear engineer. At the power plant, he provided "translation" between the plant operators and the EI software engineers, ensuring they were all on the same page.

BACK TO GRAD SCHOOL AND A FELLOWSHIP WITH NASA

Singleterry worked in that position for over four years, and he was now five years out of school. He wasn't really happy doing computer software integration, so he searched for a different path. He went to Sacramento Municipal Utility District (SMUD), hoping for a job with the reactor engineering department. "But they kept looking at my resumé and told me the computer engineering guy would love to see me," he lamented. "They basically were trying to keep me in computer science, which was what I wanted to get out of. So I knew it was time for that advanced degree."

He had lofty goals. In the back of his mind, he thought it would be great to be an astronaut. Though he wasn't a pilot, he thought he could qualify as a Mission specialist. That, however, required a PhD. He also was aware he needed to be associated with NASA somehow for any of this to happen. Singleterry reached out to one of his professors at UA, Barry Ganapol. "I just called him out of the blue one day, I think it was in October, and said I wanted to go to grad school. Are you looking for a student? And he said he had this grant with NASA, can you start in January?"

The research grant was from John Wilson, a physicist at the NASA Langley Research Center in Virginia. But when Ganapol and Singleterry started their research, they were left pretty much on their own. The grant was for research into improving the neutron component of space radiation protection to be used in building spacecraft. But, at that time, during the Reagan/Bush era, money was tight. NASA was on the back burner of the nation's thinking and funding. NASA was barely able to support the space shuttle, and the space station missions came just one vote short of being cancelled in Congress.

So, even though the NASA grant was to develop an improved model for neutrons in space radiation, this level of protection was focused on deep space travel, outside of the Earth's magnetic field. And, at that time, NASA wasn't interested in space radiation. However, the money had already been allocated to this research, "so Barry and I were trying to solve problems no one else cared about." Ganapol and Singleterry were both nuclear engineers, but they were working for a physicist. And there was a difference in the way the two disciplines looked at things.

As a physicist, Wilson wanted to explore the physics behind neutrons in radiation, but Singleterry and Ganapol were more interested in developing a solution. "Wilson just wanted a model and the physics behind it, and I just wanted to build a safe spacecraft," says Singleterry. It wasn't an ideal situation, but enough work got done for Singleterry to complete his PhD.

FINDING A JOB THROUGH SERENDIPITY

Serendipity has played a huge role in Singleterry's life. Soon after he left EI to pursue his PhD, his manager also went to work for Argonne National Laboratory West in Idaho Falls as the manager of their chemistry department. On Singleterry's first trip home to Idaho while in grad school, they ran into each other in the airport baggage claim. Singleterry and his former boss caught up a bit. "He asked what I was doing that summer, and I joked and said, 'Working for you.' It was an off-hand remark. But he said, 'Yeah. I work at Argonne, and we need you to come in because we're working on being able to analyze plutonium in our chemistry lab.'"

Just by being in the right place at the right time, and of course, asking, Singleterry had a summer internship with his former boss.

At that time, Argonne had an active integral fast reactor program, and the Department of Energy was paying for it. Part of the project was to put plutonium into the reactor. But the labs weren't set up for plutonium; they were designed for uranium research. They needed Singleterry to go through all the systems and show what needed to be done in order to facilitate the use of plutonium for analysis.

It was an old facility, Singleterry says. "Things had been added, and some of the blueprints were missing, so I had to run down systems and make sure the blueprints matched what was actually there. And we needed to figure out what the plutonium regulations were as well as some possible breaches." His responsibility would be to get the process started so they could demonstrate to the Department of Energy they were ready for the plutonium research.

Just as he was getting started at Argonne, he was introduced to the associate lab director, John Sackett, who was one of the first PhDs to come out of the nuclear engineering department at the University of Arizona. "So I had credibility before I even showed what I could do," Singleterry laughs. "And, before I even started, he said I could come back the next summer!"

Singleterry ended up with a summer job, in his hometown, with his wife, for as long as he needed, while working on his studies in Arizona. "So I went back for four summers, and they keep asking, 'When the hell are you graduating?'" He told them to give him a year to finish his dissertation, and, at the end of May, he would be able to come and work full-time. They agreed, and by November, he had an official job offer.

FUNDING CUTS LEAD TO A NEW JOB SEARCH

Not too long after, in January 1993, Singleterry was "typing furiously" on his dissertation while listening to President Clinton's first State of the Union address. During the speech, Clinton said he was going to eliminate $1.2 billion in advanced reactor research. "The only research I knew that was being done was at Argonne. And there I was, planning to go work for them," Singleterry remembers. "So the next day I called Argonne to ask if I still had a job." He was told he should still report to Argonne after his dissertation was completed.

When he arrived, the atmosphere was grim. But the lab director at Argonne insisted the work they were doing was too important for a politician to mess up, so everyone should continue with their research. And, for the first year, that worked.

However, the next year, Clinton appointees in the Department of Energy came to this director to tell him that he absolutely had to shut down. Again, he said, "no," figuring it worked the last time and it might work once more. But he was told, "If you won't shut it down, we'll find someone else who will. We'll replace you."

Singleterry recalls the director was not one to be bullied, and he responded by saying, "Okay, but let me shut it down. I'll do it the right way so we can bring it back up and continue the research when the time is right." The shutdown began during his third year and was completed at the end of his fourth year. At that point, "they told us they weren't going to need nuclear engineers anymore. I needed to find another job."

BACK TO NASA

Singleterry thought about his contacts in the nuclear industry and decided to call John Wilson, the physicist he had worked for at NASA. Even though they hadn't spoken in three years, Wilson said he could secure a fellowship for Singleterry. "I knew this would mean a big cut in pay, and, if I stayed at Argonne, I could get tenure after five years. I had almost reached that point," Singleterry says. So the money would have been much better at Argonne. But, if he stayed, he would be doing materials research, not advanced reactor research, as he hoped. He had a hard choice to make.

Then, three days later, John Wilson called Singleterry in a panic. He had found a permanent civil service job perfect for Singleterry at NASA, but the paperwork for civil service employment had to be completed right away so he could be in the running for the job.

The job was to conduct research in space radiation, which was just what Singleterry wanted to do. The finalists for the position were soon narrowed down to a nuclear engineer—Singleterry—and a nuclear physicist. Singleterry was chosen.

In August 1997, he began his full-time employment at NASA. Singleterry found NASA a wonderful place to work; instead of just paper pushing, which is typical of a civil servant job, he conducted actual research.

"Sure," he acknowledges, "I administer grants and manage a couple million dollars, so I do some paper pushing, but primarily I do research."

But that's when the problems started. Singleterry reports they gave him the job title of physicist rather than engineer. And, at this point, he began to realize Wilson had no idea what an engineer actually did. Singleterry's new job required knowledge of physics above what he already knew. "Wilson kept thinking of me as a physicist, but I'm not. I'm an engineer."

The major part of his job was analyzing space vehicles, looking to make the program codes better. Then one day, Wilson came up against Singleterry's very different approach to inputting code. "Wilson came to me and said, 'I don't know why people aren't using our code HZETRN.' I knew why."

To use the code, he had to edit it, put in the model he wanted for the materials in FORTRAN (FORTRAN is still the language of choice for high-performance scientific/engineering coding), compile it, run it, and analyze the output, a process Singleterry found ridiculously difficult. But he also realized he didn't understand how physics research worked. "I told him the physicists should do the research on what parameters were needed, and I would design spacecraft to meet requirements," says Singleterry. "I decided I could do that under Wilson, but he had to understand my approach and point of view." But they often came to loggerheads over research theory versus applying the research for practical solutions.

One of the projects Singleterry had completed was an input deck for consolidating all the inputs needed to use the existing code. "You would put in all the inputs through an input deck and, therefore, you only had to compile HZETRN once. So you could have a whole bunch of different model parameters that you could manipulate, putting in different materials, etc. And you didn't have to keep editing the HZETRN FORTRAN code, which can be a problem; when people edit manually, they can make mistakes, and those mistakes could propagate, and then, a year later, the model wasn't what you thought it was." This was the classic loss of version control.

Singleterry knew of another radiation transport code called Attila, used for vehicle research. New space vehicles were being drawn in CAD (Computer-Aided Design). The closer manufacturing came to the CAD drawings, the better the results. And Attila could pull the CAD drawings in directly. "But our code, HZETRN, couldn't allow that," Singleterry reports. Although HZETRN data couldn't be pulled into Attila, Singleterry thought it might be possible. Unfortunately, "as you'll see, it took me two years to figure out it couldn't. But that also gave me two years to think."

SABBATICAL

In 2001, Singleterry learned of a two-year NASA Administrator's Fellowship program. Wilson was not happy he was leaving, but he understood Singleterry's frustration. Singleterry decide to take a sabbatical, thinking that, during these two years, he'd find a place within NASA to do radiation engineering rather than radiation physics, and get his title changed to engineer.

He left home for two years on sabbatical to pursue this program. For the first nine months of the NASA Administrator's Fellowship program, he was at Prairie View A&M University, a historically Black College and University (HBCU), helping the college become more NASA-aware. (Prairie View hosts the NASA Center for Applied Radiation Research.) While there, he taught a class in basic nuclear engineering. The university was starting a nuclear engineering program, and Singleterry was instrumental in helping them build this program.

Singleterry ended his sabbatical at the University of New Mexico, where he continued working on his former project, attempting to get the data pulled from HZETRN into Attila. "I worked with the professors at U of N.M., and we came to the conclusion it just wasn't doable," Singleterry admits.

While on fellowship, he was trying to figure out how to make different types of analyses better using Wilson's code, which was quick—HZETRN can analyze thirty models in a day—but didn't yield the best results. Attila is much slower—it takes thirty days to analyze one model—but the results are more reliable.

Singleterry was looking at what was needed to design space vehicles from an engineering point of view—what analyses did you need? But Wilson was insisting this was not important. "Again," Singleterry says, "there was the dichotomy of how we thought about these things, each from our own perspective. I was looking down the road thinking we needed better tools for the design process, but he thought his tool was fine and could be made even better, although he didn't know how."

Unfortunately, Singleterry's work at U of N.M. turned out to be a bit of a bust. But his work gave him new ideas and helped him understand he could achieve what he hoped to in the physics world, but "as an engineer, using engineering principles and thinking, talking, and working like an engineer."

RETURNING TO NASA

After his sabbatical, Singleterry came back to NASA Langley in 2004 and told Wilson and his colleagues they needed another interface into HZETRN. His input deck, while helpful, was too difficult to put to general use. "We need a more straightforward web interface to consolidate and optimize the input to HZETRN."

This work is important in understanding how radiation will impact astronauts in spacecraft when they are in deep space where there is no magnetic field. Only eighteen people have been outside the magnetic field—the Apollo mission astronauts. But they were only outside the field for a maximum of fourteen days. Singleterry notes that, if a manned mission is sent to Mars, the astronauts will be out of the magnetic field for as long as four years. These astronauts will run the risk of receiving a potentially fatal radiation exposure during their mission. And, even if they make it back seemingly healthy, there could be a possible long-term cancer risk as a result of their mission.

Singleterry and two computer engineers developed the original front-end interface to HZETRN, which was called SIREST. They started on an improved interface, something specific and useful with which spacecraft designers could do their research. It has a simple web interface and requires minimal information input.

A few years later, Singleterry and his colleagues started looking to enhance the tool. "The underlying code for SIREST was primitive," he notes. "So I worked on a proposal to create a new web interface with more modern tools."

The result is OLTARIS (On Line Tool for the Assessment of Radiation in Space), which is still running today. However, although it is still a going concern, Singleterry notes NASA seems less interested in it than it had once been. The funding for its development came from biologists and physicists doing basic research on space radiation, but OLTARIS is an engineering tool. So, continued funding for it isn't promising. "We have nothing to replace it," Singleterry laments. "My vision for the next ten years is on what comes next. We spend six to ten months making sure you have the CAD model for a space vehicle that is useful for space radiation analysis. Then we spend a month on the analysis. I've been working since 2009 on how to cut down the many months mucking with the CAD model."

Singleterry stresses it is even more important to get physicists to understand the importance of the engineering process, because they think the problem is already handled. He offers an example from reactor power. The Manhattan Project team consisted of many top physicists and scientists, but they couldn't just take that research and make a power plant out of it. The realization of reactor power required engineers to gather the data, apply the physics of fission, and design a reactor.

"Engineers had to get involved, to take all that lovely physics, and make it useful," he points out. And, while he acknowledges the nuclear physicists he works with at NASA are wonderful and provide him with excellent data, they can't turn the data into something useful. "That's what engineers are for." And he is emphatic that this is not a negative comment. "But when physicists look at my approach and think it's a waste of time, well, that gets frustrating."

Right now, NASA is not pursuing deep space travel. It's expensive, and there isn't the funding.

Currently, Singleterry is working on analyzing vehicles from CAD drawings to determine what is necessary to go from a drawing to a definitive determination of whether or not the proposed vehicle can withstand the radiation limits it needs to endure. It's not an easy process. He notes that one problem is communication goes only one way. "I never tell the CAD guy what I need. He just puts stuff in there. The drawings look very good, but they are created by design engineers, not structural engineers, or flow engineers, or nuclear engineers. These designers aren't putting in specifics like the required thickness of pipes in their drawings, or indicating what material the pipe is made of." The consequences are significant, he explains. "We're going through the process with the vehicle, spending years going through the drawings and months doing the analysis. We have to do this faster."

He stresses they need tools to automate fixing the CAD drawings. "Right now, the engineers are using their best judgment to come up with specifics based on how different elements of the capsule might function in space." Meanwhile, he and his team are cataloging that process, figuring out what has to happen in order to effectively and efficiently take a CAD drawing and analyze it for radiation.

COMMITTED TO THE NEXT GENERATION
OF NUCLEAR WORKERS

Singleterry is committed to helping people entering the field. Once he got his PhD, he visited a number of high schools, telling them, "Look, you're here now, but this isn't where you'll end up. You're just in high school. There is a lot of time out there."

He also went to colleges and told grad students they shouldn't get a grad degree just to make more money. He wanted them to know if they didn't like what they were doing or didn't respect their mentors (and vice versa), they wouldn't finish. "That can be hard, and life often gets in the way of even the best-laid career plans. Explore everything," he advises. "Go to the nuclear medicine or engineering department and intern to see if you like it more than running a power plant. Every degree has an opportunity to explore, and only by doing that will you know what you want to do."

LESSONS LEARNED

- There is a high risk of failure in nuclear science since a lot of the work is unprecedented.

- Prior experiences can impact your career path.

- Open communication is important. Not everyone sees a problem the same way.

- Research and understand your career choice. The easiest path is not often the most fulfilling.

CPSIA information can be obtained
at www.ICGtesting.com
Printed in the USA
LVOW04s2057170316

479664LV00001B/1/P